# THE GREAT DELUGE: FACT OR FICTION?

Making Sense of and Bringing Together All the Reasonable Scientific Hypotheses and Legends of Many Cultures

## DOUGLAS B. ETTINGER

Includes paintings and chronological summary of
the catastrophic events surrounding the Great Deluge

The Great Deluge: Fact or Fiction?
Copyright 2016 by Douglas B. Ettinger

Published by:
Douglas B. Ettinger

I

# CONTENTS

i

# II.

## FIGURES, CHARTS, LISTINGS AND MAPS

# ACKNOWLEDGEMENTS

The author wishes to record his sincere appreciation for the ideas and guidance received from the undermentioned institutions and some of the more significant and influential individuals during the researching and writing of this book. Without their own thoughtful research and revealing presentations many noteworthy facts and ideas would have escaped my attention. For these numerous contributions to non-consensus and alternative science the author is truly grateful.

## INDIVIDUALS

D.S. Allan & J.B. Delair, writers of "Cataclysm! Compelling Evidence of a Cosmic Catastrophe in 9500 BC" who made a very complete compilation of the Earth's forensics and mankind's traditions and legends about the Deluge.

Walt Brown, Ph.D., writer of "In the Beginning – Compelling Evidence for Creation and the Flood" developed the concept of 'hydroplates' that jettisoned water and muck into the atmosphere and buried much flora and fauna just prior to and during the Deluge.

Robert Johnston, an independent researcher, published in a NCGT Journal an article, "Massive Solar Eruptions and Their Contributions to the Cause of Tectonic Uplift" that aided my conception of the shifting of Earth's Crustal/Mantle Shell (CMS).

Wallace Thornhill and David Talbott, co-writers of "Thunderbolts of the Gods" and "The Electric Universe" explained ancient archetypes as a manifestation of the ever-changing solar system as viewed by earlier people. The archetypes were then identified as electrical phenomena that could be produced in plasma research laboratories. Thornhill was one of the first to identify anomalous surface features on Mars as electric arc blasts.

Anthony L. Peratt, PhD Life Fellow of IEEE and member of Los Alamos National Laboratory, a plasma physicist, wrote *Physics of the Plasma Universe*. He was one of the original discoverers that worldwide petroglyphs recorded in antiquity are associated with morphological types of plasma displays created in the laboratory. His research compares high-current plasma Z-pinches and both plasma stability and instability data with prolific archetypes such as aurora funnels, stickman, big-horn-sheep profiles, and squatter man. Refer to plasmauniverse.info.

Ev Cochrane's article, "Anomalies in Ancient Descriptions of the Sun-God" was published in the Chronology & Catastrophism Review 2016:2 of the Society for Interdisciplinary Studies (SIS). Cochrane, a comparative mythologist, wrote superb, delineated descriptions of how the Sun-Gods of ancient Mesopotamia, Egypt, and India differ with our Sun today. These differences for me aligned perfectly with the visiting Nemesis star.

Andrew Hall, an independent physicist, published blogs titled "Arc Blasts" for the Thunderbolt Project group explaining electrical scarring on Earth caused by the dielectric breakdown of the atmosphere via glowing plasma figures called 'stick man'. Anomalous geologic formations such as buttes, mesas, arches, hoodoos, and flatirons were caused by electrical phenomena per Hall's explanations.

Robert Bauval & Graham Hancock championed in several publications the 'Orion Correlation Theory' and the re-dating of the Giza complex aiding the dating of the Great Deluge and true timeline of much earlier cultures in the Middle East.

Robert M. Schoch, a renowned geologist, published articles that re-date the Great Sphinx of Giza and the Bolivian complex, Puma Punku, and the Moais of Easter Island which collaborates the flood timeline. See his website - robertschoch.com.

Zecharia Sitchin, writer of "The Twelfth Planet" has, very importantly, given me the idea of a sizable celestial body orbiting the Sun every 3600 years and passing through the inner solar system causing various degrees of destruction on Earth.

Isaac Asimov, prolific writer of non-fiction, has given me a very basic concept that our Moon is really a planet, which I call the 'Moon enigma'.

Jan Pini, editor of my website and artist for my original pastel and water color drawings, has given me many skills through these recent years to survive the new internet age, and has provided immense inspiration with her graphic art and general acceptance of the possibility of paradigm shifts.

## INSTITUTIONS

Google – the technology company that searches the world's information using emails, webpages, images, and videos. Its fervent quest to remain free and independent is very laudable.

Wikipedia – a free online encyclopedia that allows anyone to have the best university library at their fingertips. Qualified volunteers constantly up-date the information.

You-tube – an American video-sharing website that presents science in its many forms from NASA space probe data, laboratory experiments, university lectures, general blogs, and, most importantly, viewpoints from independent scientists that move away from consensus science and challenge the existing paradigms.

Thunderbolt Project – the internet voice of the "Electric Universe Theory" that attempts to highlight the importance of electricity over gravity in our solar system and galaxy. This independent group of scientists has convinced me to break-away from many cherished paradigms.

PlasmaUniverse.info: This website provides publications of the IEEE Nuclear and Plasma Sciences Society. These publications include transactions on plasma science, special issues on plasma cosmology and the associated IEEE workshops. The important study of connections of laboratory experiments and computer simulations with worldwide petroglyphs recorded in antiquity can be found on this website.

# PREFACE

This book is basically a technical explanation of the legendary Great Deluge which has been explored scientifically by other authors in recent years. Evidence through both earth and space sciences is provided to support this hypothesis. The occurrences surrounding this global disaster are complicated and require some scientific knowledge at least at the high school level. This flood is not only documented in the Christian Bible but in the traditions of varied cultures on every continent. The storyline does not need to distance anyone from their belief in God. God and his ways can be manifested by the rules and laws of modern scientific knowledge. There is good reason that a God operates with these laws in mind. If you are intimidated by mixing and crossing between the physical sciences such as physics, chemistry, earth science, astronomy, and space science and the life/social sciences such as biology, archeology, and geography then this book may not be for you. There is some mathematics presented but nothing that goes substantially into advanced calculus or statistics. If you love reading about the various scientific disciplines which may lead you to this extraordinary hypothesis of the Great Deluge, then you should enjoy this book. The material is no more difficult than reading magazines as Scientific American or the Smithsonian.

The reader will be treated to numerous controversies regarding why it happened, when it happened, how it happened, and how it affected mankind's civilizations. Current consensus thinking is that the seeds of civilizations started about 11,000 years BP called the Stone Age which is after the hypothesized Great Deluge. This book regards that advanced civilizations existed thousands of years prior to the flood and were mostly wiped out. These ancient cultures cannot be well dated because the flood and other subsequent calamitous events through time destroyed their infrastructure and artifacts leaving behind only some stone megaliths and anomalous artifacts whose timelines cannot be accurately measured. Better dating methods and more data are now corroborating that ancient cultures are indeed much older than 11,500 years BP, the approximate date for the Great Deluge. This author's research will outline which ideas of previous scientists are accepted and in some cases which parts of their ideas have to be rejected.

To start the reader into an easy understanding of this comparatively recent catastrophe, various episodes or distinctly separated events will be presented utilizing a chronological and pictorial tour. These episodes are presented in a summary preceding the main book. The Great Deluge occurred during the historical transition of the Pleistocene/Holocene eras when the Holocene mass extinction occurred. The timeline for this transition goes back to the Younger Dryas geological period that is identified by various modern dating methods – chiefly radiometric and core drillings of ice sheets and sea beds. Some Biblical experts try to explain the Great Deluge based on compiling years that were recorded in the books of the Old Testament of the Jewish and Christian Bibles. This author only accepts the modern consensus dating for the Younger Dryas as the time when the Great Deluge occurred (with some small exceptions).

Please do not reject the entire storyline because you cannot accept all these events; the scope of these calamities provides a reader a chance to selectively question and create possibly even a better technical accounting of the planetary forensics presented. The preceding short tour or summary will give the reader a rough outline before delving into the more detailed text and charts of the main book. The reader must be open minded on many fronts to absorb all the details of this catastrophe that drove mankind literally back into the Stone Age.

The timeline for these events starts with the arrival of celestial visitors, the Nemesis-brown dwarf star and its own planets. More can be read about the Sun's orbiting sister star at ettingerjournals.com/dbe_mankind.shtml. On each visit both the Sun and Nemesis become increasingly active due to an exchange of electrical charges in the form of dark and glowing plasma sometimes recorded by surviving observers of the ancient sky. The fireworks in the ancient skies created from these visits by Nemesis are recorded and catalogued as archetypes by David Talbott, a renowned comparative mythologist. The Sun generated large amounts of solar wind that increasingly magnetized the Earth's dipole magnetic field. Then a highly improbable close conjunction of the Earth, Sun, Nemesis star, Mars, and one or more of Nemesis's planets created a series-type circuit of interplanetary Birkland currents that discharged onto the Earth's pre-deluge North Pole located south of the Hudson Bay. The immense electrical discharge splattered the ice sheet and launched ice shards and ice rocks onto surrounding areas eventually sputtering more deeply into rocky materials that formed the astroblemes of the Hudson and James Bays. This high energy discharge made Earth's magnetic dipole even more intense. The compilation of related events is continued with other calamities listed below:

- Movement and disorder of the ancient sky is caused by the Earth's rotation of the crustal/mantle shell (CMS) that then changed the oblateness of the Earth's surface and disrupted the surface crust causing elevation changes, earthquakes, increased volcanism, lake run-offs, and river directional changes.

- Destruction of the civilization of Plato's Atlantis occurred at this time. Atlantis sunk and was buried in the mid-Atlantic Ocean due to 'hydroplates' releasing superheated water and muck high into the atmosphere along oceanic rifts. This unique idea of 'hydroplates', subterranean reservoirs of trapped super-pressurized water, comes from Walter Brown, Ph.D., and is fully recognized by this book.

- The asphyxiation and burial of mammoths and other mega-fauna in Siberia and Alaska were due to jettisoned steam and muck from the 'hydroplates' freezing in the upper regions of the stratosphere in the north polar region before falling with ferocious, high density onto the latitudinally relocated landscape.

- Dramatic uplift and destruction of Puma Punku, an ancient, but advanced industrial complex in Bolivia, on top of a plateau in the Andes mountain range was due to the accelerated expansion of subterranean heated rock including its coincidental phase change.

- Sinking of the Land of Mu, large island chains with advanced cultures, into the Southern Pacific left behind only small clusters of exposed tips of volcanoes now called the Polynesian Islands. Inca traditions claim that their first leaders came from the sea, most likely from Mu.

- Finally, the most culminating and best-known event is initiated. The East Antarctica ice sheet sinks, then floats, and slides on top of a slush layer calving into the Southern Ocean to cause the Great Deluge. The existing ocean level rose in steps finally achieving about 395 feet higher than the previous antediluvian level and wiping out most of mankind's advanced civilizations if not already destroyed by previous horrific calamities.

- Squatter or stick men, glowing / stable electrical discharges between the ionosphere and the Earth's surface, electrically sputtered rocky material to mysteriously form buttes, mesas, and pinnacles in the Southwest and in other high plateau regions worldwide. The energy transfer also melted subterranean rock to bubble upward and produce anomalous hoodoos and arches.

- Flatiron-rocks were formed from supersonic plasma electric-dust storms that deposited triangular shaped layers against mountain ridges worldwide. This abundant electrical energy in the ionosphere is eventually bled-off into the Earth's magnetosphere tail which spreads into the realm of the Sun's heliosphere bubble.

The ionosphere raised to pre-existing heights, and normal electrical activity resumed.

A pictorial review provides a broad-brush outline of the more important calamitous events that surrounded the Great Deluge. Remember, that the trigger for these events are celestial intruders which are predicted to keep returning periodically, but hopefully not always creating such unspeakable tragedy for life on this planet.

# PREFACE ADDENDUM

(A Preface Addendum is inserted to explain new research and the evolution of thought that occurred since the first release in 2017 into the *EttingerJournals.com* website.)

As I write this paper in late 2018, enough time has passed to judge the validity of some of my original hypotheses expressed in *The Great Deluge: Fact or Fiction* written in 2016. It is important to comment on some changes in thought that occurred due to recent research and the awareness of new ideas by others. These new ideas came primarily from Robert Johnston in his article "Collaborating Massive Solar Eruptions Causing Catastrophism on Earth" published in the NCGT Journal in 2014; and, from Andrew Hall's "Arc Blasts -Parts 1, 2, and 3" articles found in thunderbolts.info/wp/2016/05/11/arc-blast-part-1. Johnston predicted that super-mega corona mass ejections (CME's) struck the Earth, shrunk the magnetosphere against the ionosphere, and supplied enough electrical energy to heat the tectonic boundaries. This in turn thermally and ionically expanded the rock in those regions to dramatically uplift the already existing mountain ridges and plateaus in a synchronous, rapid fashion. Hall, on the other hand, predicted that supersonic ionic dust storms created the flatiron rocks and other mysterious landscapes such as buttes, pinnacles, hoodoos, and arches on elevated plateaus. Induced volcanism may have supplied much of this dust, but certainly the stickmen (worldwide glowing archetypes) sputtered away rock surfaces to produce most of the electrified dust required by Hall's hypothesis for the Southwest's landscape, in particularly, flatiron rocks.

These concepts were fully adopted to further corroborate my Great Deluge hypothesis and the Nemesis star. The Nemesis star hypothesis presented in ettingerjournals.com/dbe_mankind.shtml and a follow-up paper, ettingerjournals.com/dbe_sun_gods.shtml are now required even more for producing Robertson's anomalous CME's. What Robertson lacked was the needed electrical interaction of a predicted brown dwarf star and the Sun which dramatically triggered new activity in the Sun to produce intense solar winds and then finally super-massive corona mass ejections. The predicted amount of energy in these CME's, $1 \times 10(29)$ ergs, is enough to jerk and rotate or change the angular momentum of the crustal-mantle shell (CMS) of the Earth. The hypothesis requires that previous intense solar winds further magnetized the dipole magnet of the spinning Earth's crustal/mantle shell (CMS). Amazingly, the combination of these events exactly produces the amount of predicted rotation of about 23 to 25 degrees for the CMS due to vectorially magnetic field interaction.

A reason can be given for the prior intense solar winds because the visiting Nemesis star feeds electrical energy into the Sun as it crosses the helio-magnetosphere 10's of years ahead of its known arrival into the inner solar system. The significance of Robertson's mega-CME hypothesis is explained in more detail at ettingerjournals.com/dbe_solar_eruptions.shtml.

My previous thoughts were that a magnetic coupling occurred between the Earth's overly magnetic crust and the close encounter with the magnetic field of a passing planet. This may have been a contributory factor, but was questionable about how the necessary amount of energy could be transferred to move the Earth's CMS. However, Robertson's concept much improves that prediction and is absolutely stunning. The random, but well aimed CME not only provides enough energy to change the angular momentum of the CMS but also produces roughly the amount of rotation that was already predicted in my hypothesis. This amount of rotation is the angle that the Earth's tilted axis makes with the ecliptic plane, the source of the CME's organized magnetic field. However, my concept that the archetype, the Cosmic Wheel with a tongue, still remains. The conjunction of Nemesis and various planets connecting Birkland currents did destroy the Laurentide Ice Sheet with high energy arc blasting.

Another evolved thought was synchronous uplift of the western mountain ranges of North and South America. At first, I attributed this uplift solely to the shift of the tectonic plates jerked quickly westward being carried over the edges of the heavier oceanic plates. The reason for this rapid movement of the plates was due to the latitudinal rotation of the entire CMS. The horizontal vector forces parallel to the crust above the slippery Moho layer and the change in Earth's oblateness combined to produce this stunning synchronous uplift. However, Robertson's concepts of the highly electrified and heated rock layers at the tectonic boundaries caused expansion both thermally and ionically due to phase changes of the molten rock are now added to my version. Robertson's concept definitely lends more credence to anomalous, dramatic and synchronous uplifts of the crust.

Hall's prediction corroborates beautifully how the worldwide appearance of 'stickman' was caused by Robertson's charged ionosphere coming from the super-massive CME's. 'Stickmen' represent the dielectric breakdown of the atmosphere between the charged ionosphere and Earth's crustal surface. The effects of the 'stickman' arc blasting and sputtering rock ionically as pointed out by Hall created the buttes, mesas, pinnacles, and peculiar deposits of level, diverse, colored sediments found in the USA's Southwest. This calamity also caused the supersonic, electrical dust storms that created the flatiron rocks to be deposited against various worldwide mountain ridges.

In summary, Robertson's and Hall's concepts, have brought together the hypotheses of: 1) the Nemesis' star; 2) the electrified and magnetized Earth's CMS and ionosphere; 3) the rotation of the CMS by about 23 degrees via the interaction of intense magnetic fields; 4) the changing geoid or oblateness of Earth's crust; 5) worldwide crustal disturbances including dramatic elevation changes; 6) the sinking of the Antarctica landmass that released its ice sheet; 7) the ocean level rising to create the Great Deluge; and 8) thus, taking all these calamities together, explains how most of mankind's existing ancient, advanced civilizations were destroyed.

# PICTORIAL AND CHRONOLOGICAL SUMMARY OF THE CATASTROPHIC EVENTS SURROUNDING THE GREAT DELUGE

This summary is divided into 12 major events that occurred before, during and after the Great Deluge. These events overlap each other, but some definitely happened before others. An attempt is made to place them in an approximate chronological order as is postulated to have happened. Original painted drawings, one for each event, portray what any possible survivors might have witnessed. Hopefully, the reader survives an accounting of these horrific events and is then prepared to read the main book.

## 1.

## CELESTIAL VISITORS' ARRIVAL ON THE EDGES OF THE SOLAR SYSTEM

Celestial disturbances are normally attributed to infrequent mass extinctions and other global catastrophes. But what are these intruders and where do they come from? Are these deadly meddlers - meteor storms, large asteroid strikes, close encounters of a rogue planet, or mega-corona mass ejections from the Sun? The forensics of Earth's last great catastrophe, the Holocene extinction event occurring close to the end of the Younger Dryas around 11,500 BP reveals clearly the origin and credentials of this interloper. The interloper is an undetected, captured brown dwarf star that orbits the Sun several hundreds of years each time for unknown millions of years. Other evidence of its identity is given by discoveries made by space probes to both major and minor planets in the Sun's system. Repeated electrical scarring on most of the other planets and moons indicate that our Nemesis visitor has transgressed and released thunderbolts of energy during each crossing, (the sign of the cross), toward different victims with varying degrees of destruction leaving behind irregular moons, asteroids, comets and rings around major planets. The star is very electrical and magnetic stealing energy from the galaxy and making exchanges of energy with the Sun as its orbital path takes it away from the Sun. When Nemesis comes close again it releases energy at the Sun's heliosphere that may cause the Sun to become super-active depending on the current flow direction. Electrical engineers combining ideas with some astrophysicists now

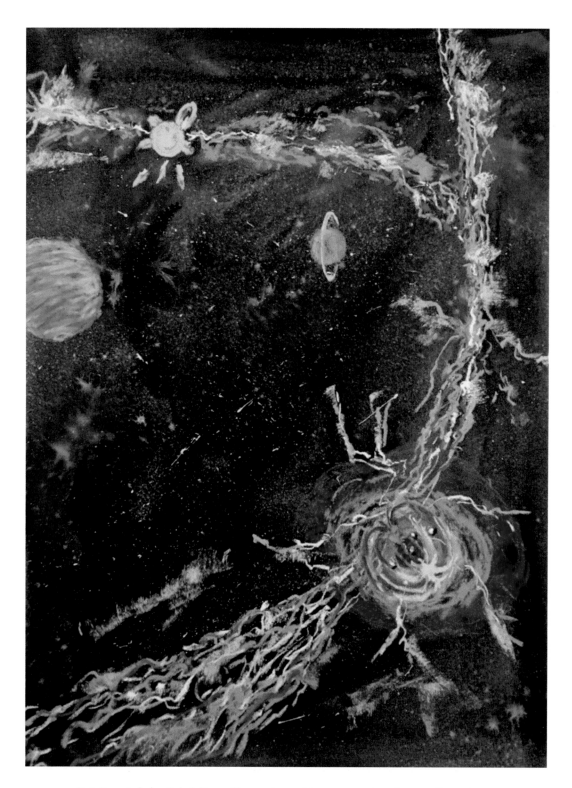

Painting 1: Celestial visitors, Nemesis and her consort, arrive on the edges of the solar system after orbiting her sister star, the sun, another 3,600 or more years.

believe the Sun is a large anode having cathodic planets that are interconnected by solar winds and other dark plasma currents. Although the electromagnetic affects dominate the calamities between Nemesis and the solar system bodies, this fearful goddess has its own planets that can cause the perturbance of existing asteroids which then may collide with the Sun's planets and moons.

Nemesis' orbit is roughly determined to have an apoapsis beyond the Plutonian minor planets at about 470 AU. Its closer periapsis is somewhat variable, but believed to occur somewhere between Mars and Saturn and above the ecliptic plane. Havoc begins when the brown dwarf with its sizable dim corona crashes through the heliosphere of the Sun. More than likely, electrical charge imbalances occur that discharge themselves via Birkland currents of humongous streams of electrons and ions along the heliosphere interface that then rush toward the magnetic dipole of the Sun's polar regions. This clashing of their electrical circuitry begins perhaps hundreds of years well before humanity knows of Nemesis' arrival amongst the Sun's planets near its periapsis. The effects of Nemesis' coming are revealed by the activated solar winds causing disturbances with the Earth's weather, climates, earthquakes, and volcanic activity. Famine, plague, drought, and the weakening of man's infrastructure may well precede Nemesis' appearance in the sky. What happened during the Great Deluge catastrophe, is that Nemesis and its corona region released extremely large amounts of charge toward the Sun. The Sun became overly active. At first many sunspots, solar flares, and unusually large amounts of solar wind were released. These solar winds affected the planets' own magnetospheres, especially the closest terrestrial planets such as Earth. Eventually the Sun received too much electrical charge from its sister star and began to belch mega-size coronal mass ejections (CME's). Unfortunately, one or more of these mega-CME's were directed toward Earth which eventually created the Great Deluge.

## 2

## THE CONJUNCTION AND CLOSE ENCOUNTER OF EARTH, NEMESIS AND OTHER PLANETS

The catastrophe of 11,500 BP was compounded by the alignment or conjunction of several celestial bodies. This conjunction created for a short period of time what the ancients called the "Cosmic Wheel" archetype of an ancient sky. The briefly aligned bodies of Earth, Mars, possibly a Nemesis planet and Nemesis itself were seen from Earth as three or more concentric bright circles with a dark spot in the center. The dark spot in the center was probably Mars; the next concentric circle was probably flaring of large density electrical discharges passing around another planet's surface on its journey to the lowest ground state which was Earth's past magnetic polar region centered on the Laurentide ice sheet. The next concentric circle was Nemesis' brightened corona surface. The corona surface may have shown briefly various phases due to light reflection and impacting solar winds from the Sun. The wavy or straight spiked flares and the different moon-like phases were all characteristics of the Cosmic Wheel.

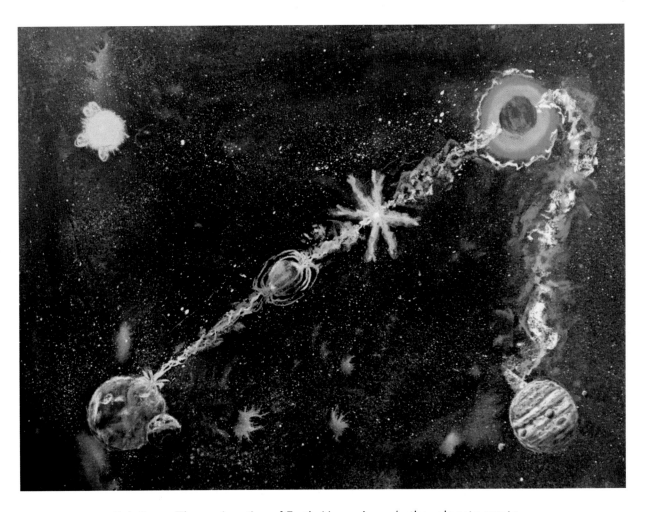

Painting 2: The conjunction of Earth, Nemesis, and other planets create an electric circuit that is seen by mankind as the cosmic wheel in the ancient sky

Jupiter or Saturn may also have been particularly closer to Nemesis on this visit and fed the brown dwarf more energy due to their charge imbalance via Birkland currents. This temporary charging allowed the CME's from Nemesis to reach pass its own corona's boundary. An electrical series circuit was created because of the unusually and highly improbable alignment of all the previously mentioned charged celestial bodies.

Consequently, Earth's past polar region received a very bright plasma discharge that appeared as a "Cosmic Wheel with Tongue" archetype. The tongue reached to the edge of the northern horizon and was the electric discharge that blew apart the Laurentide ice sheet and created the Hudson and James Bay astroblemes. The increased charge from the solar winds and the arc blast of Birkland currents on the North Pole also intensified the electrical charge of the Earth's crust including its sea water, subterranean waters, the electrically conductive plate boundaries, and its Moho layer. The spinning Earth with this extra electromagnetic energy created a more powerful dipole magnetic field which would soon react with another temporary stronger magnetic field coming from the Sun's recently released mega-CME's.

# 3

# HIGH ENERGY ELECTROMAGNETIC PLASMA DISCHARGE SPUTTERING THE LAURENTIDE ICE CAP

A convincing, documented claim is made by scientists of the ElectricUniverse.com that the celestial bodies have different build-ups of electric charge - the Sun being a positive anode, and the planets generally being negative cathodes. Circuitry between these bodies is created by a dark plasma, called the solar wind, which carries both positive ions and negative electrons. If conditions are ideal, high energy plasma discharges can occur between these bodies due to an unbalance of charge similar to static electricity or lightning. The discharges through interplanetary space are accomplished by Birkland or double-layer currents that are still considered impossible by consensus science. This circuitry is witnessed today by auroras correlated with Sun activity and the recent discovery of individual magnetospheres of the Sun and its planets.

The highly improbable conditions were just right prior to the Great Deluge to cause an immense discharge between either a close encounter of an unknown, highly charged and magnetized planet or the conjunctions of various planets with Earth and the Nemesis star that completed a series circuit ending with a highly directed discharge. The spin-axis pole was then located east and south of the Hudson Bay in Canada which was the center of the ice cap or ice sheets that covered Canada, Greenland, and northern USA. Electromagnetic factors would cause the crustal/mantle shell (CMS) to rotate about 20 to 30 degrees latitudinally thereby moving the spin axis under the center of the Arctic Ocean and under the center of Antarctica. In turn, the fractured Laurentide ice sheet moved southward into a temperate zone to accelerate its continued melting and demise. At the South Pole the Antarctica land mass sank releasing its giant ice sheet into the ocean.

Painting 3: High energy electromagnetic discharge destroys the Laurentide Polar Ice Sheet and gouges the rocky surface to form the astroblemes of Hudson and James Bayes.

This violent, plasma thunderbolt of unbelievable scale would strike the Laurentide Ice Sheet and sputter large shards and chunks of ice into various trajectories. The high energy would eventually cut through the thick ice and sputter rocky crustal materials, too. This final excavation of rock would create the astroblemes of the Hudson and James Bay, and create the huge, mysterious megalithic stones spread randomly over the northern hemisphere called erratic rocks. The trajectory of the ice shards and ice rocks created global phenomena of concentrations of oriented shallow depressions with little indication of meteorite fall. This undeniable evidence of ejected sputtered ice from the Laurentide ice sheet caused the unusual clusters of elongated, shallow craters. Some are listed: the Carolina bays on the southern coastline of the United States; the Nebraska rain basins; the lakes in the Alaskan permafrost near Point Barrow; the depressions in the Beni region of north-eastern Bolivia; the aligned lakes of the Old Crow Plain west of the Mackenzie Valley in Yukon, Canada; the river valleys of Penzhina and Anadyr in north-eastern Siberia; and, the unexplainable structures in the Netherlands.

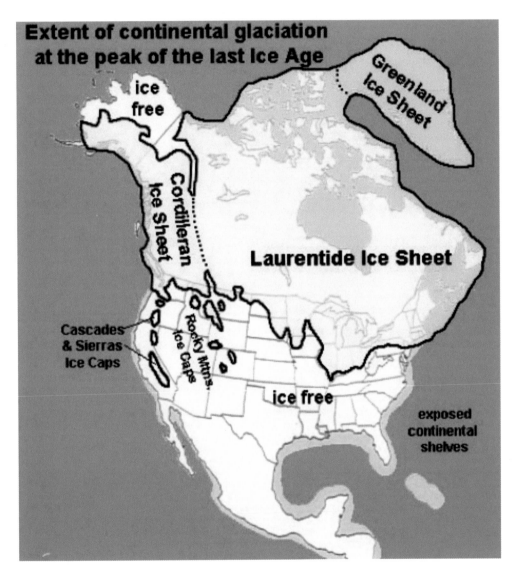

Figure A: Laurentide Ice Sheet was the ancient polar region before the rotation of the crustal/mantle shell occurred (*from GotBooks, MiraCosta.edu*)

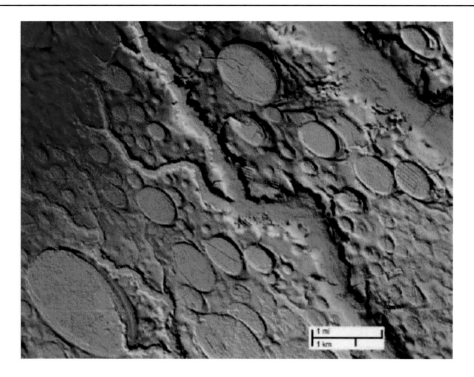

Figure B. North Carolina bays' orientation pointing toward James Bay,
Canada (*from ancient-origins.net*)

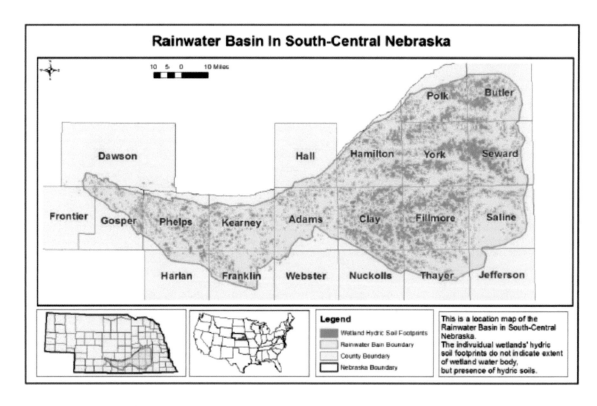

Figure C. Nebraska rain water basins elongated and oriented toward
Hudson Bay (*from WDAR elevations for playa wetlands; awramedia.org*)

Figure D. Nebraska rain basin using Lidar elevation map technology (*from cinto.org*)

Figure E1. Samson's Putting

Additionally, immense electrical currents with high voltage would travel from the base of the thunderbolt along major North American rivers and sea coasts to electrocute fauna and flora and create general conflagration throughout the continent. Sediments of black carbon in river valleys give evidence of this occurrence.

Figure E2. Some examples of erratic rocks that occur mysteriously in random fashion everywhere in the northern hemisphere (*from geocaching.com*). Many readers have surely visited erratics and wondered about their origins.

The resulting fractured, calving, and electrically heated Laurentide ice sheet would provide more ice and water inventories to dramatically increase ocean levels that added to East Antarctica's losing most of its ice sheet into the Southern Ocean. Any glaciers left from the splitting of the Laurentide ice sheet would quickly (meaning about 100 years) melt due to its general movement from an Arctic to a Temperate Climate Zone.

# 4

# COSMIC WHEEL ARCHETYPE LAUNCHING OF
# THE HOLOCENE MASS EXTINCTION

The famous Cosmic Wheel archetype with a tongue and wavy spokes is thought to have commenced the horrific events that led to the Holocene mass extinction and demise of the

Painting 4. The conjunction of Nemesis and planets displays the cosmic
wheel archetype which launches the holocene mass extinction

Clovis people in North America. This same event is directly connected to the Great Deluge. Archetypes of man's recorded icons viewed in the ancient skies were developed by David Talbott, a comparative mythologist. His archetypes are seen in rock art (petroglyphs), cultural traditions, friezes carved into rock of ancient temples, adornments of various ancient leaders, and actual written descriptions. One special archetype known worldwide is the Cosmic Wheel with various configurations such as straight or wavy spokes, concentric circles, and/or a projecting tongue reaching to the horizon. The author of this paper postulates that this archetype was the Nemesis star and/or planet(s) that due to either a close

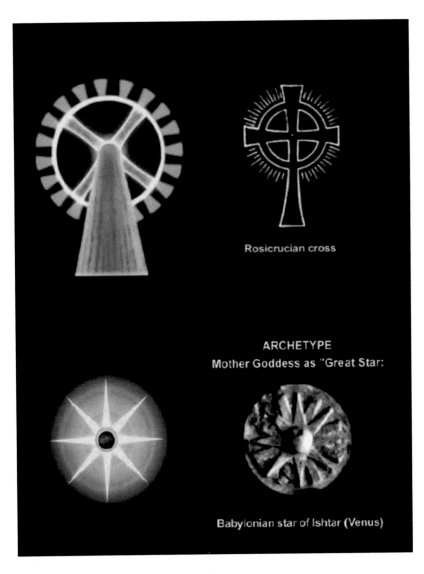

Figure F. Various versions of the cosmic wheel archetype are shown
(*from pinterest.com and by Symbols of an Alien Sky*)

encounter or a conjunction of several celestial bodies discharged immense Birkland type currents of glowing plasma toward planet Earth. The concentric circle(s) represented a corona structure and/or conjunction(s) of other planets; the spokes depicted electrical instability and flaring of the brown dwarf star or a planet in the path of the conjunction. Depending on various distances from Earth the cosmic wheel for a small length of time could have appeared without wavy spokes or a tongue reaching down to Earth.

As the electrical circuitry between these celestial bodies became organized a tongue eventually appeared directed toward the Earth from the northern sky. The glowing tongue was the discharge of electrical currents directed magnetically at the Earth's north pole. At the base huge pieces of ice from the Laurentide ice sheet were sputtered outward into the atmosphere into various trajectories. Currents of electricity followed the Earth's surface southward especially through conductive waterways creating fires and other destruction. The ejected ice rocks then struck Earth's surfaces in various locations creating shallow, elongated, parallel, oriented craters with no rims. The ice then continued to break-up into smaller shards that continued their deadly scattering and destroying of flora and killing any animals in its path.

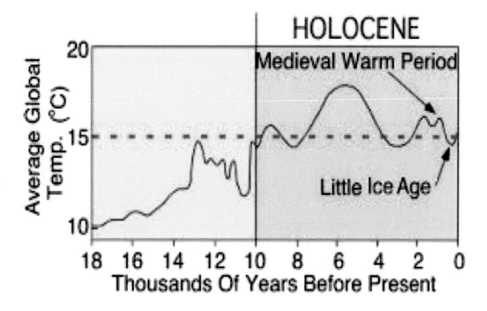

Figure G. The indicative dip in temperature prior to the pleistocene/holocene boundary is known as the Younger Dryas; the end of this period marks the holocene extinction event and the Great Deluge (*from phys.org*)

This combination of fire, lightning, electrocution, and bombardment of ice rocks and shards along with the subsequent flooding wiped out the Clovis people. The consensus by anthropologists is that some unknown catastrophe destroyed their civilization; but they cannot agree on the cause. Clovis settlements with the famous, distinct arrowheads ceased to exist in radiocarbon dating and sediments younger than about 9000 to 11,000 years ago. At this same time many megafaunas in North America also went extinct such as the rhinoceros, camel, giant sloth, and saber-tooth tiger. The pieces of the puzzle of this horrible tragedy can now be assembled.

## 5

## MOVEMENT AND DISORDER OF THE ANCIENT SKY RESULTS IN THE CRUSTAL/MANTLE DISPLACEMENT

For the Earth's crust/mantle shell (CMS) to move about 20 to 30 degrees perhaps over about 4 hours of time, the movement of the sky was definitely visible and noticeable in the nighttime sky or with the Sun and/or Moon still in view. Since the crust/mantle shell moved latitudinally the Sun, Moon, and star trails would appear to have roughly vertical derangements and either sink into the horizon or rise above the horizon. Indeed, an ancient Chinese epic recounted that the "Sun, Moon, and stars poured down into the northwest where the sky became low". Obviously, if Asia moved closer to the North Pole as the crust rotated, then China was experiencing summertime with the Sun overhead, before it sank toward the horizon. This same epic then proceeds to tell how "rivers, seas, and oceans rushed down to the southeast, where the Earth sank." This narration confirms how the pre-deluge equator near China moved southward, thus elevating the crustal geoid and draining water from shorelines southward due to centripetal force. Finally, the epic explains the final stage of destruction by stating, "A great conflagration burst out. Flood raged." The conflagration was caused by a combination of electrical currents moving on the surface, severe lightning, and possibly falling, burning meteorites originating from the cosmic wheel's tongue sputtering crustal rocks. Then the Flood finally arrives being the very last calamity which makes certain causal sense. The depiction above of a Chinese landscape also shows meteors with wavy tails thought to be serpent or dragon archetypes. These visions are really melting ice rocks erratically dispersing a trail of water vapor as they travel through the atmosphere.

Painting 5: Movement and disorder of the ancient sky is evidence of the crustal/mantle shell rotating about the Earth's liquid core and disrupting surface elevations on its changing geoid

The Roman, Ovid, tells how the Chariot of the Sun driven by Phaeton moved "no longer in the same course as before". More than likely, Phaeton is attributed to the actual Nemesis brown dwarf star in this myth. Ovid's epic confirms the movement of the sky by stating how the constellations of the Cold Bears tried to plunge into the ocean. Of course, the Roman writers took their stories from the earlier Greeks who wrote about their own so-called legends handed down from hundreds of generations.

Figure H. For humans after the rotation of the crustal/mantle shell (CMS)
the background of stars with respect to the moon's and sun's path would
change; hence, the constellations of the zodiac also changed

There are many other traditions that explain the movement of the sky. The more described ones are from the Eskimos, from a Norse saga, and the Ute Indians of California. Celestial derangements are recounted on all continents and are mostly connected to the Great Deluge and/or celestial-visitor myths. There can be only one undeniable conclusion: Earth's crust/mantle-shell did rotate thereby causing a global flood. These so-call myths are actually real stories with embellishments that are found worldwide; and, indeed, corroborate each other with their coincidental descriptions of calamitous events.

## 6

## DESTRUCTION OF PLATO'S ATLANTIS TRIGGERED BY THE ERUPTION OF THE MID-ATLANTIC RIFT

Plato wrote about the lost island civilization of Atlantis that ruled the ancient world in the Mediterranean region and competed with the Greeks for control. Its location was described

Painting 6. The Destruction of Plato's Atlantis was due to 'hydroplates' erupting at the mid-Atlantis Rift and sinking and burying an advanced civilization into the deep ocean.

as being beyond the pillars of Hercules which was known in ancient times as the strait between the Mediterranean Sea and Atlantic Ocean. Speculation led to its location being in the middle of the Atlantic Ocean directly westward of the Iberian Peninsula. Further speculation leads me to believe the island or a series of islands were the raised mid-Atlantic Ridge that is now revealed by underwater mapping. This ridge could have been partially exposed in pre-deluge times similar to Iceland of today.

From this vantage point the Atlanteans could have controlled the waters of the Atlantic for colonizing the Americas and Africa and fighting wars with their contemporaries, the Greeks, in the western Mediterranean that existed well before the times of Solon, Plato, and Socrates.

Plato vaguely based its destruction occurring 9000 years before his time. He wrote his dialogues about 360 BC which quoted Solon who visited Egypt in 590 BC and translated their records. This adding of previous years places the flooding and sinking of Atlantis very close to the end of the Younger Dryas which is the postulated time of the Great Deluge of 9500 years BC.

Figure I. Atlantic Ocean floor, 1977 (*by Heinrich Barann*)

So, what are the technical possibilities that could have led to its demise? I strongly believe that Walt Brown in his book, *In the Beginning*, adequately explains a series of steps for the cause. His hypothesis reveals "hydroplates" which are large subterranean reservoirs of trapped super-critical high-pressure water that Earth's geology created along many of the oceanic rifts that separate the tectonic plates. These rifts create distinct uplifted ridges under the ocean and are above sea level in some places such as Iceland. Some of these rifts occur on continents. These rifts are postulated to be the origins of the edges of tectonic plates where the continental crusts drift apart from each other. The Earth's crustal/mantle shell was displaced or rotated about the outer core and resulted dynamically in pulling apart many of these rift boundaries. Super-critical water of very high pressure held underneath the crustal plates was then released and jettisoned upward very high into the atmosphere. The water carried many dissolved minerals that were formed via tidal forces on the reservoir floors over eons of time. The subsequent 'waters from the Deep' separated Atlantis into two parts and covered it with scalding hot sediments of muck. The subsequent Deluge waters submerged these ridge islands. Then static forces of the muck and additional head of flood water collapsed the roof of the "hydroplate" ceilings thereby slowly sinking the covered Atlantis into a very deep ocean. These superior intellectual Atlanteans were merely the victims of circumstance – call it fate. The global degradation of human intellect after the Great Deluge probably led the surviving Greeks to believe in the myths of their deities that were superior to any others and destroyed the evil Atlanteans; these myths embodied the ideal state of the Greeks which Plato wrote about in, *The Republic*. These deities, later adopted by the Romans, also personified the celestial bodies for reasons learned about in the study of the Nemesis star presented in ettingerjournals.com/dbe_mankind.shtml.

# 7

## ASPHYXIATION AND BURIAL OF SIBERIAN MAMMOTHS CAUSED BY FALLING HAIL AND MUCK

The asphyxiation, quick-freeze, and burial of mammoths and other megafauna in Siberia and Alaska has loomed as one the greatest mysteries in the natural history of the planet. This mystery has spawned several theories about the poles quickly shifting. However, this author has postulated a very specific rotation of only the crustal/mantle unit for about 25° of latitude to explain a rapid and permanent climate change in these northern lands. The spin axis orientation was preserved by the gyroscopic stability of the inner and outer cores of Earth. Siberia was in pre-deluge times a grassland with trees very suitable for grazing animals. Then its climate converted quickly to an arctic tundra region with permafrost and only small stunted bushes. This phenomenon occurred over only about 4 hours creating - huge storms and in many cases quick-freezing for the mammoths. The final calamity, the global flooding, caused the receding water and the piling of mammoth bones on islands along the northern shoreline of Siberia; and, the heaping of uprooted trees and animal bones sometimes 200 feet high called yedomas. The strangeness of this paleontology is only explained by the subsequent and final calamity, the onslaught of the Great Deluge.

More improved evidence of their demise comes from Walt Brown's book, *In the Beginning – Compelling Evidence for Creation and the Flood.* Brown postulated that 'hydroplates' (his own concept and term) contained huge amounts of hot, pressurized super-critical water trapped in subterranean reservoirs under most of the world's uplifted oceanic ridges or rifts. Continued accelerated tidal forces eventually heated the water to enough temperature to release and jettison this water upward into the atmosphere and fall back to Earth with muddy minerals swept from the reservoir floors. This fallen hot muck would create sediments that buried much flora and fauna. My version differs in that a celestial disturbance causes a crustal/mantle displacement (not continued tidal heating as Brown suggests) which then disturbs and opens many rifts like a zipper. Another major difference between Brown and myself for the fallen "waters from the deep" is that many extinct animal species found themselves rotated into the newly created Arctic region. The muck that befell them was frozen containing sleet and/or hail. The shallow seas of the Arctic Ocean allowed the

Painting 7. The asphyxiation and burial of mammoths in Siberia is caused by falling frozen muck generated by material jettisoned from 'hydroplates' under the Arctic Ocean into the upper polar atmosphere.

jettisoned water and minerals from the 'hydroplates' to be ejected higher through the atmosphere closer to the ionosphere. As it began to fall the water had time to freeze. This frozen muck fell onto the regions in Siberia and Alaska where the mammoths and other large animals grazed or hunted. This massive high-density muck-fall froze the animals while both smothering and burying them sometimes before they could even fall down.

Figure J. Arctic Ocean floor showing oceanic ridges that are hypothesized to have released super-critical steam high into the atmosphere during the Holocene Mass Extinction (*from natgeomaps.com*)

Brown's analysis of 'rock ice' corroborates his hypothesis extremely well. Rock ice is found in and around mammoth remains. This strange ice has a yellow tinge and rounded elongated bubbles with no dissolved air and easily-seen embedded dirt and plant particles. Brown attributes the yellow tinge to minerals that were pulled from the 'hydroplate' reservoirs; the bubbles with no air is attributed to water freezing well above the atmosphere where little air exists; and, there is proof that the ice was never part of a frozen lake or stream since the organic materials would settle out before freezing occurred. Furthermore, frozen-food experts claim that to preserve the mammoth flesh, the outer layers of skin would have to drop suddenly to -150 to -175°F. Such a required heat sink in a Siberian summertime can only come from the airless stratosphere which reinforces Brown hypothesis for 'hydroplates' and my hypothesis that the entire region rotated into a new Arctic zone.

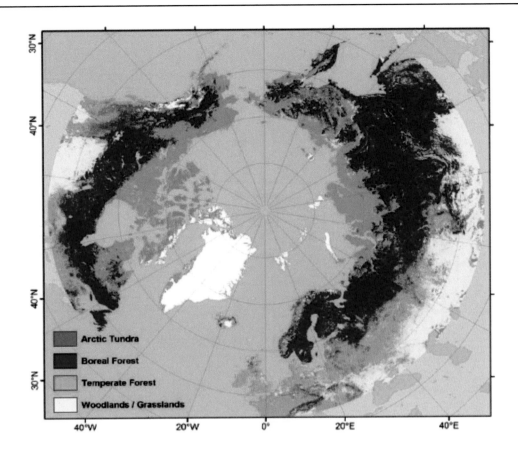

Figure K. Arctic tundra and boreal forest in Siberia and Alaska that once upon a time were temperate forest or grasslands before crustal/mantle shell (CMS) rotation (*from pinterest.com*)

Massive lightning strikes occurred on the edges of the muck-fall storms due to static electricity of highly kinetic ionic ices and dust in the atmosphere. These high energy strikes caused massive fires on the fringe of muck-falls that are proven by carbonization of certain layers of sediment. The final Flood would then extinguish these fires on the grasslands not covered by muck-fall. The mystery of the mass extinction of many faunas in these regions at the beginning of the Holocene era is resolved. Also, other megafauna in the United States of America were also driven into extinction due to other distinct calamities following the huge electric discharge over the Laurentide ice sheet. All these extinctions are roughly dated to have occurred during the same time period surrounding the boundary of the Pleistocene and Holocene epochs.

8

# DRAMATIC UPLIFT AND DESTRUCTION OF PUMA PUNKU INSTIGATED BY THERMAL EXPANSION OF ROCK

Painting 8: Dramatic uplift of Puma Punku in the Bolivian Andes was fashioned by tectonic plates pushed together causing immense heat and electrical conductivity that then produced material phase changes and expansion in the subterranean rock

Puma Punku is a group of amazing megalithic structures near Tiwanaku, Bolivia, located on a 13,000-foot high plateau in the Andes Mountains. These sandstone structures are three-dimensional interlocked blocks of various shapes that are now in a random, tumbled, scattered disarray with many of these manmade stone structures buried under thick layers of harden sediments. Many of these stone slabs have machined (inferred) flat surfaces with a rough surface on the opposite side; these machined surfaces are of various shapes of rectangular or H-shape blocks having accurate 90° corners, slots, blind round holes, and square holes. Some of these stone blocks measure as much as 25 feet by 17 feet wide by 3 feet thick weighing almost 130 metric tons that were quarried as far as 56 miles away. This amazing masonry is characterized as accurately cut or molded rectilinear blocks of such uniformity that they can be interchanged. I-shaped architectural special alloy clamps are either cast or hammered in situ to connect many of the largest slabs. This same technology of clamping is also known to exist in ancient Egypt's dynastic-pyramid building period of 3000 to 2000 BC. Tunnels, channels, walls, open reservoirs, platforms and one-piece gates are all parts of this complex. Some archeologists have postulated that this campus is some kind of industrial complex for an ore processing plant since many precious metals such as gold, silver, copper, and tin have been discovered and mined through the ages in this region. This may be the reason that Spanish Conquistadores found great quantities of gold and silver held by the Incas with no explanation to its origin.

Consensus archeologists date these structures backward to the proposed beginning of the Inca civilization at 200 to 300 years AD; however, it is believed that the Incas of Tiwanaku with their bronze-age technology could not possibly have made these stone shapes which even challenges modern man's technology. Recently, a geologist, Dr. Robert Schoch, has dated these structures to about 11,700 years BP when catastrophic damage occurred. Schoch's dating methods are difficult to refute (see robertschoch.com). Some large rock slabs of gate-type structures were cracked apart during a violent movement of the ground; the rough surfaces within the cracks have been both weathered and encrusted with lichen that provides a good dating method. Also, some discovered tunnels have developed stalactites which produce accurate dating of 12,000 years or more.

This unbelievable data challenges current dogma and gives way to the credence that an ancient civilization prior to 11,700 years BP had developed skills and tools equivalent or better than our modern technology. It is obvious that this destruction occurred near the dating of the Great Deluge of the Younger Dryas. The demise of this civilization was due to calamitous events prior to or immediately following the flood. So indeed, the total destruction of Puma Punku is evidence that severe earthquakes, mudslides, and a sudden uplift of this Andes plateau, called the Altiplano, occurred. It is predicted that Puma Punku was very close to current sea level when the entire western South American shoreline with sudden synchrony uplifted to create the Andes Mountain range with high altitude plateaus. Puma Punku is believed to have lifted on a horst or elongated block from a level close to sea level to its present elevation of 13,000 feet.

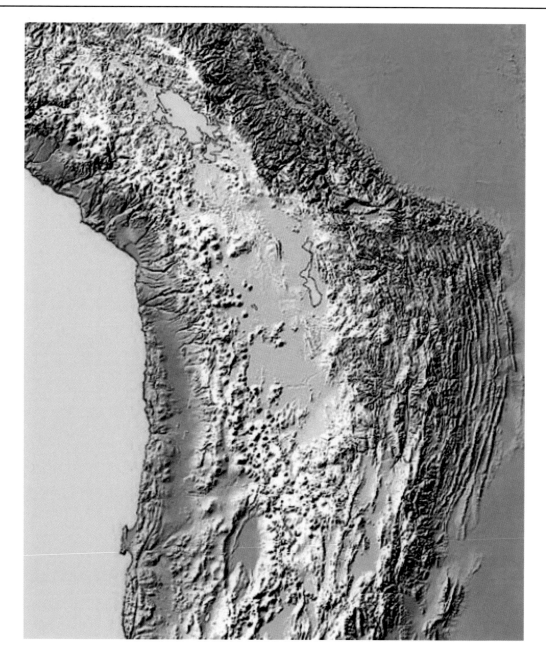

Figure L. The Altiplano of Bolivia and Peru showing Lake Titicaca (*from geoscienceworld.com*)

There is evidence of unexpected sea creatures in Lake Titicaca. Discovered species of seahorse, corals, and certain seashells could only come from ocean sources. The Altiplano Bolivian plateau and its lakes were originally at sea level gathering thick sediments of salt. Most of the Altiplano was covered by ancient Lake Tauca that included Lake Titcaca and Solar de Ulyuni, a huge salt flat. Sequential transformation of drainages between several vast lakes were dated occurring in periods 13,000 to 120,000 years ago. The youngest prehistoric lake was radiocarbon dated to 11,500 to 13,400 years BP. These lakes were sometimes repeatedly refilled and then emptied to form ever thicker salt flats. About 14,200 years ago, lake levels dropped before rising again until 11,500 years ago. During the Great Uplift of 11,500 years BP, Puma Punku was most likely easily reached from the ocean by bays and rivers. Ancient Lake Tauca may have continued until 8500 years ago. These changing lake levels provide proof that some dramatic climate and radical topographical changes occurred most recently centered near the 11,500-year BP time period.

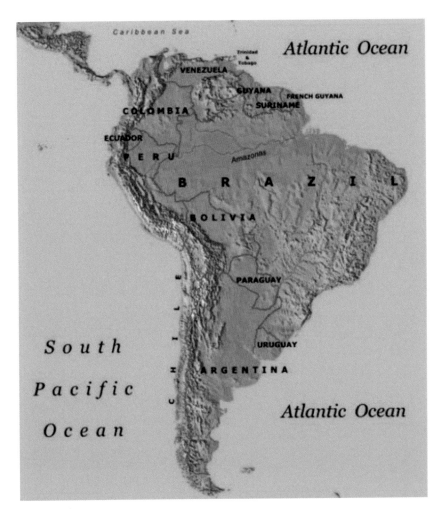

Figure M. The entire Andes mountain range was suddenly uplifed together (*from Free World Maps Collection*)

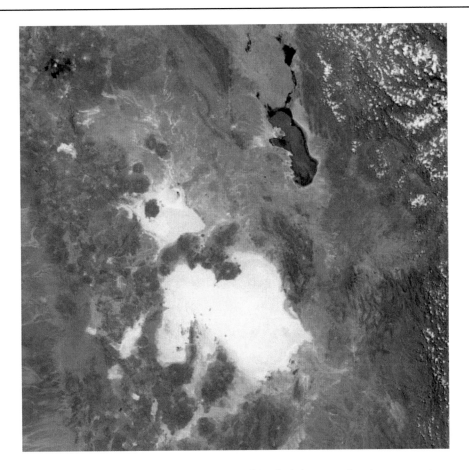

Figure N. The remains of raised lower-altitude lakes are dry deserts and salt flats; Salar de Ulyuni, a huge salt flat, is shown in the center of the Altiplano Plateau (*from Salar de Uyuni screenshot_5.png*)

Slower, more continued uniform recovery took place until today. Specifically, the sudden rise of the Andes Mountain ridges and the Altiplano in Bolivia - 1) caused a rain shadow due to recently risen ridges creating drought conditions on the eastern leeward side; 2) caused ground movements stopping drainage from the deepest Lake Titicaca; and, 3) caused partial tilting and/or damming in the plateau to drain or dry-up certain lake regions during different time spans. These phenomena could have possibly occurred several times from 120,000 years ago causing the Andes Mountains to rise in several dramatic levels. The final calamitous step occurred 11, 500 years BP near the time of the Great Flood. So, why did these mountainous ridges rise suddenly and together?

The model for this Great Uplift is given by the crustal/mantle shell (CMS) rotation causing violent subduction of Pacific tectonic plate boundaries, and the expansion of crustal materials due to thermal and phase changes postulated by Robert Johnston (bob.johnson1000@gmail.com) in his article: "Collaborating Massive Solar Eruptions Causing Catastrophism on Earth", published in the NCGT Journal, V2, No. 1, March 2014.

My response to Johnston's article is found at ettingerjournals.com/dbe_solar_eruptions.shtml. The energy for these events is supplied by the increased solar winds and eventually the arrival of super-massive CME's from the over-active Sun. The electrical energy supplied the heat energy along preferred conductive pathways at tectonic boundaries to decrease crustal material densities and raise the surface.

The magnetic energy of the CME's caused the crustal-mantle-shell (CMS) to rotate causing a clash of vector forces to quickly move the South American plate above the Pacific oceanic plate. The destruction of Puma Punku setting on a plateau of a suddenly raised horst can only be explained by these means. Other rapidly raised horsts are the Colorado Plateau at 6000 feet elevation that created electrical etching of the landscape that predates the Hopi people, Lake Texcoco at 7300 feet elevation near Mexico City that was drained and predates the Aztec with human occupation measured at 11,100 years BP; and, Lake Humboldt at 8400 feet elevation near Bogota, Columbia that was drained and had human occupation at 12,460 years BP. All these combined coincidences can only mean that a catastrophic uplift of the tectonic plates bordering the Pacific Ocean did actually happen.

# 9

# SINKING OF MU IN SOUTHERN PACIFIC INITIATED BY SUDDEN ELEVATION CHANGES OF THE CRUST

Mu is a name popularized as a lost continent by 19th century Augustus Le Plongeon who claimed Mu was the home of its refugees who fled catastrophe and founded several ancient civilizations. The concept was expanded to include lost continents in the center of three oceans. Later the idea matured with James Churchward asserting this continent was in the center of the Pacific. (*Wikipedia/Land of Mu*)

This paper differs with these debunked concepts by having Mu as a cluster or series of both small and large islands formed by both raised oceanic ridges and isolated volcanoes in the South Pacific. These large islands were spread over an area now known as the Polynesian islands that exist roughly within a triangle defined by Hawaii, New Zealand, and Easter Island. There were no lost continents. The island sizes were greatly diminished by the events of a crustal/mantle shell rotation and the Great Deluge of 11,500 years BP. Modern geological knowledge that rules out 'lost continents' does not pertain to this newest concept which accepts crustal/mantle shell rotation and the resulting sinking of islands.

Painting 9. Sinking of the Land of Mu located on large island chains in the southern Pacific was due to sudden elevation changes in the crust created by the rotation of Earth's crustal/mantle shell

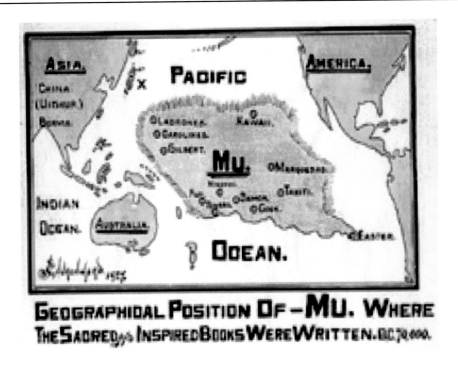

Figure O. The continent of Mu envisioned by James Churchward

Figure P. The ocean floor shows raised ridges in the south Pacific Ocean that were once part of Mu (*from earthlymission.com*)

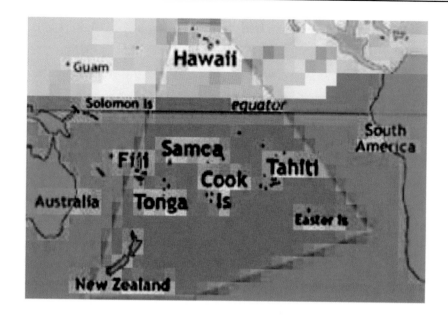

Figure Q. The Polynesian Islands' triangle map of today are the tips of land masses that sank and destroyed the Mu civilization (*by pinterest.com*)

This highly advanced civilization of Mu, not assumed to be the origin of man's first civilization as with Churchward, communicated with other ancient civilizations in the Americas, Indonesia, and southern Asia during its existence. Today's Polynesians are partially descendants of these peoples. Transfer of knowledge between these Polynesians and peoples in Central America (the pre-Mayans and pre-Aztecs) and the pre-Inca of South America is recounted by the characteristics of their sculptures, DNA origins, and traditions telling similar stories.

Survivors of the Great Deluge on Easter Island had delusions and yearnings for the Mu leadership returning to their island and thus re-acquiring their past glory. An obsession developed for making huge stone statues of "ahu's" and "moai's". These Easter Island people used their fading memories of past technical knowledge to honor and welcome the returning Mu people and the spirits of ancestral leaders. In doing so, they depleted all resources of wood by cutting down all the island's trees. These people were then trapped on Easter Island because of its remoteness and having no more materials to build boats. When they first saw Europeans, they rejoiced seeing boats made from wood arrive on their shores.

The Nazca people in Peru lived on the suddenly raised Nazca plateau during the Great Deluge period. They created large geoglyphs on the dry desert surface with lines of rocks and removed surface soil that could only be seen from a great height. They were hoping to signal to the returning and remembered gods of Mu. Perhaps the people of Mu had knowledge of and used flying craft that made the Nazca people make large animal pictorials only seen from the sky. Their progenitors left possibly because of impending disasters – never to return – leaving the people confused. Like modern day cargo-cults they tried to call their Gods by drawing lines, trapezoids and figures.

Not as well-known are similar surface geoglyphs in California. The same cultural ideas for communication possibly collaborate that the people of Mu had contact with coastal peoples of both North and South America and possibly Meso-America.

Figure R. Complex of Pictorials on the Nazca Plateau (*from peruadventuretours.com*)

The pre-deluge equator rotated about the center of these islands in the South Pacific during the crustal/mantle displacement. This rotation of the region caused the sinking of oceanic crusts due to the lessening of centripetal forces because the equator was now moved away some distance either north or south. This subsequent crustal upheaval increased volcanic activity causing lava flows on top of the oceanic crust to further sink the islands. And, then the final global flooding occurred which over time sank the islands even more due to isostatic loading; in many cases the islands would rise again to greater heights above ocean level after the flood waters receded. The oceanic crust and the islands on top rose due to the lessening of the water's isostatic loading.

Figure S. Nazca line pictorial of a spider (*from images by express.co.uk*)

Numerous Polynesian traditions collaborate this concept of a sinking Mu. Samoan islanders remember both the sea rising and the sinking of the land. The new earth then arose from the womb to create the existing islands which is technically possible as previously mentioned. Tahitian tradition disclosed disobedience to their main god, Taaroa, who then sank Earth below the sea leaving behind a few 'aurus' (projecting points) which comprise the present cluster of islands. The ancient Hawaiians speak of lands stretching almost connected from their islands to Samoa, Rarotonga, Fiji, and reaching as far as New Zealand. All these island groups were called by one name, Ka-houpo-o-Kane. (Traditions taken from the book *Catacylsm! By Allan & Delair*)

The most recent claim for Mu is the sunken realm of megalithic structures located off the coast of Yonaguni Island near Okinawa in the East China Sea. These massive blocks of rock with right angles and parallel surfaces are on average 100 feet below sea level. A Japanese scientist, Masaaki Kimura, believes he can identify a pyramid, castles, roads, monuments, and a stadium; he surmises that this submerged complex may be part of the mythical Mu. *(from Wikipedia/Mu(lost continent, and /Yonaguni Monument)* The general sinking of this global region is expected technically since these underwater ruins are located on the ancient pre-deluge equator. When the equator moved about 25 degrees latitudinally northward the surface of the crust sank predictably hundreds or even several thousand feet and rested below current sea level.

Geologically, the Tongan Islands are either a limestone base created from an uplift of coral formations or a limestone overlaying a volcanic rock base. This fact makes these islands some of the oldest in Polynesia *(from Wikipedia/Geography of Tongan Islands)*. Coral reefs are normally generated underwater surrounding a rising volcanic island and when the central volcano sinks due to isostatic loading coral buildup can begin to fill-in the center of the island. Then an unexplained uplift of this island cluster created the present geological conditions which take much more than 10,000 years to perform - unless some catastrophic conditions ruled. The Tongan islands display the dynamics of sinking and rising islands in the Pacific - from the weight of volcanic islands sitting on oceanic crust; from the vertical crustal movements due to the rotation of the crustal/mantle shell; and, from the Great Deluge with the resulting isostatic vertical motions of the crust.

Archaeology of Samoa uncovered major findings of buried settlements, stone and earth mounds, Lapita pottery remains, and pre-historic artifacts dating to 10,000 years or more. The mounds (some partially or fully submerged) are rectangular pyramids, truncated with steps with some that are star shaped. Their official dating is more than 2000 years old and are known to be built over much older structures. The largest mound and most ancient Polynesian structure is Pulemelei or Star Pyramid that measures about 346 ft. x 314 ft. by 40 ft. high *(Wikipedia/Archaeology of Samoa)*. The culture's infrastructure can only be thought as a smaller imitation of other known ancient civilizations with megalithic structures throughout the world that were all tragically destroyed by the Great Deluge.

Figure T. The star-shaped pyramid or Pulemelei Mound built from basaltic stone (*from wmf.org/Pulemelei ancient mound*)

Densely populated, inland, prehistoric settlements on Samoan and Tongan islands had stone walls and raised walkways and platforms. These settlement patterns occurring inland were followed by later settlements along the coast after the earliest European arrival. Why did these island people prefer this predominant pattern of inland settlements? Possibly, their traditions of a great flood kept them from building more permanent structures along the coastline. Oral traditions made the Great Deluge all too real and always threatening for these islanders.

# 10

# EAST ANTARCTICA ICE SHEET CALVES AND SLIDES INTO OCEAN DUE TO SINKING OF CONTINENT

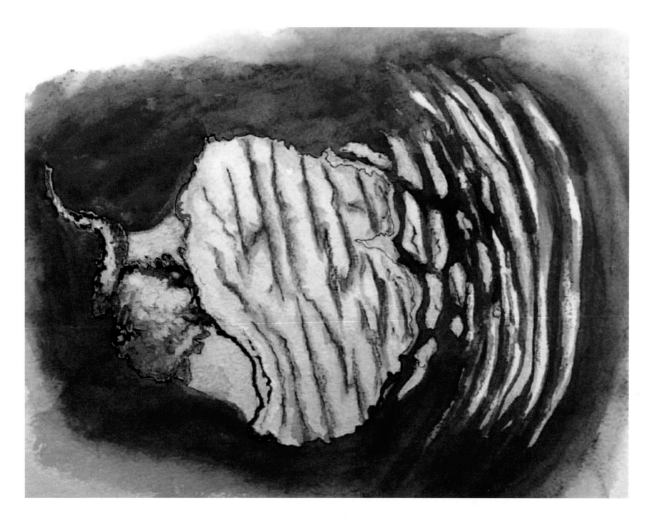

Painting 10. East Antarctica ice sheet calves and slides into the ocean because the underlying crust sank, causing the ice to slip on the phase transition of a slushy boundary and begin floating. The ice sheet thereby released its connection to the land and began to float, causing the ocean to rise.

Antarctica is the seventh continent centered on the South Pole at the Earth's spin axis. During pre-deluge times the Pole was positioned off East Antarctica's shore in the Southern Ocean toward Australia. West Antarctica did not have large ice sheets being far enough from the Pole. But Tasmania and southern New Zealand had ancient glaciers due to their closeness. During the crustal/mantle shift of 25 to 30 degrees which moved the East Antarctica landmass over the unaltered spin axis, the crust sank below ancient sea level. The landmass elevation dropped because the Earth's geoid or previous oblateness abruptly caused the crust to drop by one to two miles. Due to a slush layer created by phase changes of high pressures located deeply under the ice sheet, the ice became unstable and started to slip on this slush almost with a smooth shear boundary. Dynamic lateral forces and the rising ocean lifted and slid large parts of the ice sheet into the ocean causing humongous calving of pieces larger than the land areas of typical states of the USA. The ice being 3 to 4 miles high left the support of the land mass and began floating on the ocean. Quickly, sea level rose globally like dropping ice cubes into a glass of water. The resultant deluge would submerge the world's land masses at lower elevations. Most of mankind's developed civilizations were inundated by an estimated 395 feet rise above pre-deluge sea level which was then approximately minus 120 feet.

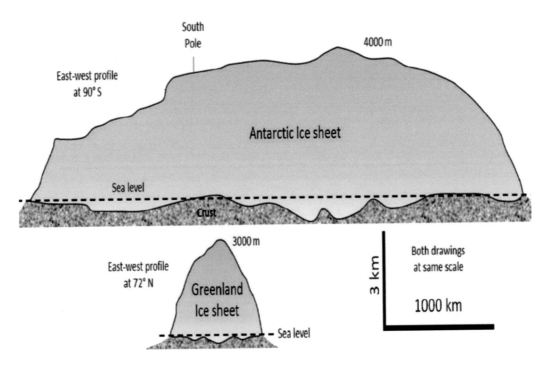

Figure U. Present ice sheet profiles (*from courses.lumenlearning*)

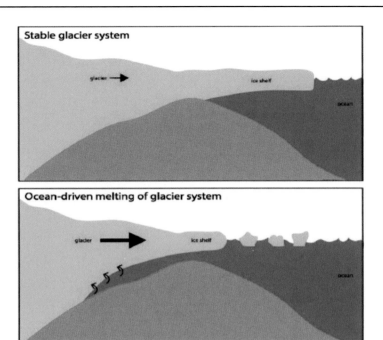

Figure V. Effects of seawater undermining ice sheet (*Antarctic ice sheet dynamics from link.springer,com*)

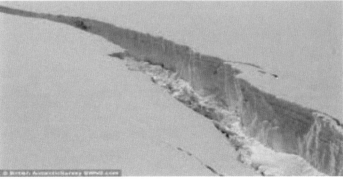

Figure W. Examples of ice sheet splitting apart and moving laterally (*Greenland ice sheet fared in 2017 from carbonbrief.org*)

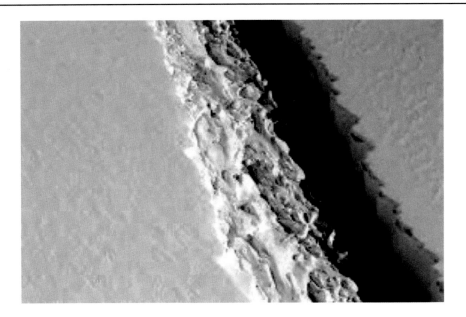

Figure X. Giant Antarctic ice shelf crack (*from scientificamerican.com*)

This dramatic flooding has been recorded on all continents by most cultures in their traditions and legends. The well documented Holocene extinction event of 11,500 years BP was aided by this catastrophe among other calamities that occurred. In the following several hundred years the ocean receded as the waters were recycled by evaporation and condensation to replenish ice sheets on Greenland, and both East and West Antarctica, and build an ice cap over the Arctic Ocean. Ice core data of East Antarctica gives dating of deep ice being about 800,000 years old, but this ice is below the slush layer that remained on land. All ice above this postulated now non-existent slush layer slid into the ocean during the Great Deluge. The land mass dramatically rebounded above sea level after the weight of most of the ancient ice sheet was gone. And, then a new ice sheet was re-formed on top of the 800,000-year-old ice which is now at least 10,000 years old.

## 11

## STICK MAN ILLUSTRATED BY PETROGLYPHS ELECTRICALLY CREATES THE SOUTHWEST LANDSCAPE

The United States' Southwest has very startling and puzzling landscapes. Existing today are unexplained buttes and pinnacles like those in Monument Valley. There are hoodoos, blind holes in cliffs, and arches like those in Arches National Park. There are perfectly horizontal layered distinct sediments with volcanic materials between sandstone layers, and dense stony aggregates lying between finely grained sandstone like those seen in Canyonlands that make

Painting 11. Squatter or Stick Man creates buttes and pinnacles in the southwest by electrically sputtering even layers of rock and depositing the generated ionic charged dust into the adjacent regions where it re-crystallized into distinct substrates.

no sense when considering its timeline. Recently, many scientists now attribute these formations to powerful electrical phenomena and not from the consensus, standard model of wind and water erosion.

But it must be understood that a rapid series of events creating these landscapes occurred both before and then following the Great Deluge. The global flooding never touched these areas due to their higher elevation, but subsequent immense electrical storms did continue throughout the deluge period at the end of the Pleistocene to completely drive the local fauna and Clovis people into extinction.

Figure Y. Monument Valley displays sandstone buttes and pinnacles setting on top of sediments of sandstone surrounded by a very level plateau. The buttes have caps of similar stone at the same elevations. No wind or water erosion or volcanoes caused these structures (*from ar.wikipedia.org*)

Figure Z. Arches, hoodoos, and horizontal holes were photographed at Arches National Park. These rock structures appear to have been very soft-like putty before crystallizing into hard sandstone. Electrical energy and ionic diffusion are possible causes. Electrical current discharge between a conductive aquafer and a lowered ionosphere caused materials to rise like a fountain to form these hardened hoodoos (*photographed by D. Ettinger*)

Figure AA. Immense electrical dust storms 10 to 100 times the power of normal lightning sorted and layered materials on top of pools of water or underground aquafers that then blew holes into the sides of forming cliffs (*photographed by D. Ettinger*)

Figure BB. A view of Canyonlands shows the dendritic excavation of material that can only be created by powerful electrical discharges between conductive layers in the crust and the charged ionosphere. The sputtered materials are then evenly deposited elsewhere, possibly creating higher layers of sediment as is shown in the photograph (*photographed by D. Ettinger*)

The sequence of events that causes the Southwest topography may have repeated itself at other times spanning millions of years prior to the Holocene time boundary which is now described. A high energy glowing plasma thunderbolt struck the pre-deluge north polar region and leashed strong electrical currents along waterways, coastlines, and plate tectonic boundaries where the most conductive conditions and pathways existed. One such tectonic boundary bordered the Pacific plate that ran continuously from Alaska to the southern tip of South America. The global surface and sub-surface electrical currents were attracted to the more conductive regions of smashing tectonic plate boundaries, the heated Moho layer beneath these regions, the surface lakes, and subterranean aquafers of the already existing raised plateaus - thereby providing feedback for evermore conductive properties and the ever-increasing attraction of electrical current. The Southwest was especially conductive being close to plate boundaries, being elevated toward the electrified ionosphere, and having aquafers both on the surface and in subterranean pools formed by melting mountain glaciers in the northern Rocky Mountains.

The electrical heat thermally expanded the underground crust in these formations ionically producing new chemical compounds by decreasing the density of certain species of minerals. Large regions of this plateau would then dramatically increase in volume rising evenly together to the elevations of today. The overactive Sun kept generating more solar wind which kept feeding the Earth's polar region and sustaining electrical current with high voltages along increasingly conductive and hotter pathways.

Then another highly improbable event quickly followed. The Sun released super-massive corona mass ejections (CME's) which were aimed unfortunately and randomly toward the Earth. This highly dense and magnetic structure of charged ions and electrons washed over the Earth's protective magnetosphere and shrunk it until it made contact with the ionosphere. Then the charged particles created a ring current approximately around the Earth's ecliptic plane and magnetically pulled the Earth's crustal/mantle shell (CMS) into alignment since its magnetic field was aligned along the spin axis that was oriented about 23 ½ degrees to the ecliptic plane. This re-alignment probably took place for 4 hours or more and caused the oblateness of the Earth to change over a comparably short time. The new geoid or oblateness created both lateral and vertical movements in the crust on top of the overheated and now slippery, less viscous Moho layer.

The more important issue for the Southwest is that it was elevated and acting like a lightning rod with the overly charged ionosphere. The Rocky Mountain plateau had an extremely heated and highly conductive aquafer along with the ionic diffusion of subterranean materials. This combination would lead to the break-down of the atmosphere's dielectric properties between the now lowered and highly charged ionosphere and the very conductive crust. The breakdown is comparable to large currents discharging between two capacitor plates and being constantly fed by huge energies supplied by one or more of the Sun's super-massive CME's (estimated at $1 \times 10^{39}$ ergs each) that traveled to and enclosed the Earth's atmosphere.

These sustained discharges between the so-called capacitor plates would be comparable to lightning bolts 10 to 100 to 1000 times the scale of today's lightning. These high voltage currents formed magnetic fields and glowing plasma configurations in the sky that appeared to surviving witnesses as immense stickmen or squatter men standing on the ground with several raised arms and squatting legs. These stickmen had glowing heads at their terminations in the clouds. To the human survivors these stickmen appeared as giant gods walking on the land and destroying everything in sight. The stickmen's feet were sputtering the plateau surfaces fairly evenly as they ejected each layer of sediment high into the atmosphere. These charged sediments would then land elsewhere to form other harden coalesced sediment beds of uniform layers. As the materials cooled re-solidification of the rock matrix took place.

In many places as the level plateau was being etched, larger electrical currents would break through from below the surface to form gushers of molten rock which formed buttes or fulgurites. Fulgurites today are created by lightning fusing vitreous materials formed of sand and other sediments. Also, hypothesized is that special caps of sediment above these buttes and pinnacles were already hardened and changed ionically to resist the etching process thus allowing these small areas to remain at their present elevations creating the buttes we see today. Whichever model is correct – fulgurite formations or a shielded etching process –, nevertheless, high energy electrical discharges were responsible for this amazing landscape.

Proof of these stickmen is recorded not only in the Southwest but world-wide. There representations are drawn on cliff and cave walls and are coincidentally very similar. This primitive rock art, called petroglyphs, are found well distributed in the Earth's middle latitudes along elevated landmasses as is shown by the following map.

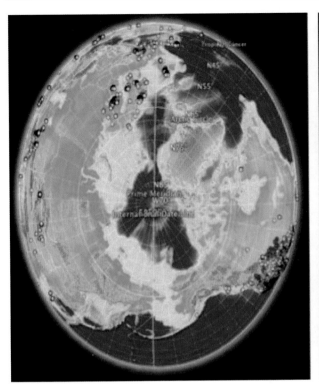 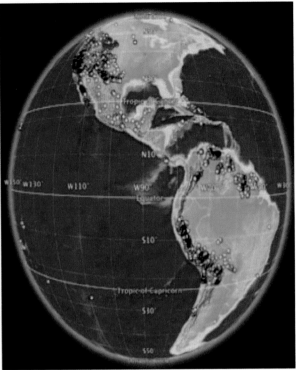

Figure CC. World Map Showing the Known Locations of Stickmen's Petroglyphs (*from plasmauniverse.info/NearEarth*)

The locations reveal lower latitudinal and equatorial regions that do not identify with any polar regions. This rock art is found mostly in high plateau mountainous regions which act like lightning rods. These high spots are not only closest to the upper dusty atmosphere and highly charged ionosphere but are directly sitting on electrically conductive subterranean wet and molten crust. These witnessed stickmen represent the break-down of the atmospheric dielectric characteristics and the sustained discharge of high voltage current between the ionosphere and high plateaus being etched or sputtered away. The specific glowing plasma configuration is sustained by magnetic fields forming around strong Birkland currents linking the ground with the lowered ionosphere.

Figure DD. Some Rock Art of Stickmen with Multi-arms at Lower Left Side Photographed in the Upper Colorado River Canyon. (*photographed by D. Ettinger*)

Figure EE. These Australian petroglyphs, unlike stickmen, probably represent polar electrical discharges where witnesses had the vantage point of looking more upward into glowing plasma instead of sideways. Also, polar discharges would be configured differently (*from australiangeographic.com.au*)

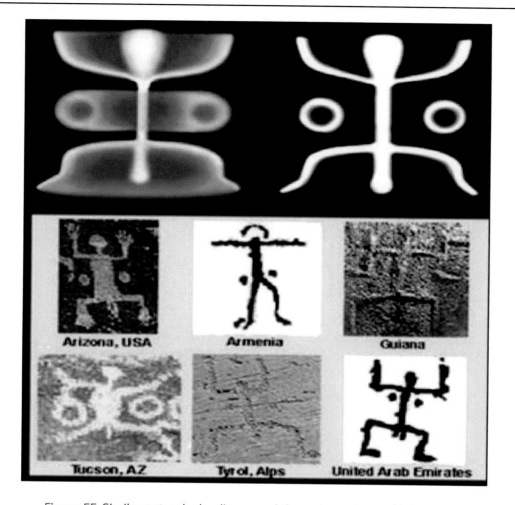

Figure FF. Similar petroglyphs discovered throughout the world that represent the stick or squatter man which resemble a unique plasma discharge configuration. These plasma configurations can be produced amazingly in present day laboratories between two oppositely charged plates (*from The Squatter Man-Plasma Connection by ancientexplorers.com and from Oldest Petroglyphs Discoveries by viewzone.com*)

A technical analysis and breakdown of the stickman is found through experimentation in a plasma laboratory. The body represents plasma filaments called Birkland currents that have a spiral of ions separated by a spiral of electrons moving in opposite directions. These currents separate near their source in the ionosphere and their terminus on ground looking like arms and squatting legs. A self-constricting ring of magnetic field forms around these currents to create diocotron instability or electron vortices. This plasma instability is a region of turbulence that changes through different forms due to the temperature, density, electric field strength, and magnetic field strength. A so-called 'sausage' instability displays harmonic variations of beam radius along the beam axis. The survivors of these horrendous electrical storms could only see the brighter cross-sections which appear as multi-arms and/or circles of axial hollow toroidal shapes symmetrically placed on each side of the stickman's body.

The base or feet of the stickman are continuously etching or sputtering away the ground surface as the Birkland currents move laterally across the surface. The excavated materials are electrified, launched high into the atmosphere, and deposited at large distances away to form other plateaus with fairly level and even sediments as are seen in Canyonlands. This charged rain of dust and rock covered aquafers and lakes that then belched and burped viscous hoodoos, arches, and blind holes in cliffs as are seen in Arches National Park.

The Southwest is proof of a highly electrified crust and ionosphere. Such a required large energy source can only be external to the Earth. The energy source has to come from the Sun in the forms of energetic solar winds and corona mass ejections (CME's) that were aimed at Earth. The connection between these stickmen and the global deluge is the immense power that is made possible by these CME(s). This estimated power of $1 \times 10^{39}$ ergs creates a magnetic ring around the Earth along the ecliptic plane to jerk the Earth's spinning magnetic dipole and rotate the crustal/mantle shell (CMS) by about 23 ½ degrees to align with the CME's magnetic ring. These estimated power values have more than ample energy to change the angular momentum of the CMS. Consequently, a reason is given for the change in the Earth's oblateness that in turn changes the polar regions and causes the East Antarctica Ice Sheet to slip into the ocean.

The Southwest terrain and the stickmen are a direct link to the Great Deluge. The extinction of the Clovis culture and the link of Southwest's rock art carvings took place around 10,800 to 12,800 years ago which encompasses the time period for the postulated Younger Dryas era and the Great Deluge. Each petroglyph site records a certain plasma event according to the unique angle of observation. A system of phonetic sound symbols (an alphabet) is associated with certain petroglyphs that produce reasonable translations using a proto-Canaanite language. The translations describe the need to take shelter from a painful vertical light and a poison coming from the sky. Hopefully, the Sun stays less violent and friendlier in the future when the Nemesis brown dwarf star visits again.

## 12

# FLATIRON ROCKS ARE FORMED FROM SUPERSONIC ELECTRIC PLASMA STORMS BOUNCING OFF RIDGES

Painting 12. Flatirons rocks are formed from high energy plasma electric storms that traveled supersonically bouncing off ridges. An electrical capacitance was formed between the ionosphere and highly conductive and recently raised mountainous plateaus; electrical polarities between regions acting similarly to battery terminals were also largely responsible.

Throughout the world there exist strange rock formations called flatirons that are strangely similar and occur repeatedly in a line across one side of a mountain ridge. These rocks are generally almost vertical cliffs but slanted between 90 to 45 degrees. Their shapes are like the bottoms of old fashion clothing irons, thus their name derivation. Many of these formations have striated coloring that remains the same for entire groups of flatirons. Some of the better-known formations are shown below.

Figure GG. Flatiron rock formation in the state of Colorado (*from bouldercoloradousa.com/things-to-do/insider-guides/flatirons*)

Figure HH. Flatirons in the Serranía de Hornocal of Jujuy Province, Argentina showing even continuous striations of colored layers (*from Wikimedia Commons, the free media repository; File:Serranía de Hornocal up close near Humahuaca.jpg*)

Figure II. Flatiron range just outside of Boulder, Colorado (*copyright Michael Collier; hosted on the AGI Earth Science World Image Bank*)

Figure JJ. Example of charged ionic dust-laden winds re-depositing horizontally (*Quebrada de Cafayate, Salta Argentina*)

Figure KK. These flatirons look like stacks of pancakes standing on their ends.

Very little consensus exists to explain these colossal natural monuments. Geologists generally claim that vertical sediments of sedimentary and/or metamorphic rock were caused by the opening of faults in the crust thereby causing these rocks from above to fall on their sides. Geologists' explanations are very weak in helping us understand how continuously identical flatirons are aligned and piled against each other having consistent shapes and layers of separated colored minerals. Without allowing for electrical phenomena for causes other explanations are not plausible.

Andrew Hall (thunderbolts.info/wp/2016/05/11/arc-blast-part-1/) has studied these formations near his home in the southwestern United States and concludes they result from arc blasting or catastrophic mega-electrical events occurring close to the Earth's surface. Hall uses terms such as ionic storms, energetic ground currents, vortex winds of Marklund convection, and supersonic tsunami-like winds of dust which move horizontally and strike the sides of highly charged existing mountain ridges. The ions being electrically heated separate into certain molecular structures to create the layers of color striations. The usual triangular shapes are caused by the transient effects of unstable wave forms and reflecting shocks which can be reproduced in the laboratory. No means of wind or water erosion or rock slides can explain these evenly almost vertical series of flatiron configurations.

Hall shows wind tunnel experiments that produce sand dunes with the same triangular wave forms as flatirons. 'U-tube' wind tunnel videos show sonic winds forming triangular and diamond shaped standing waves. Hall claims these pressure patterns in the shock wave are incredibly unique and surely cannot be called a coincidence. Hall considers these experiments are proof of his theory about flatirons. But of course, a high energy plasma environment is required which is indeed postulated by Robert Johnson and his cited Gold Theory that a super-mega solar corona mass ejection washed over the Earth's magnetosphere which then collapsed and pushed against the ionosphere.

The buttes and pinnacles of the Southwest topography are formed by arc plasma blasts between the ionosphere / charged cloud cover and the conductive ground surface. These plasma displays looked like stick or squatter men to the few well located human survivors. But it is not known whether any petroglyphs represent the horizontal electrical storms that created flatirons. The ensuing dust created by their etching and sputtering of stickmen on the surface then blended with normal local weather cells and electrical fields to create supersonic horizontal dust winds that moved between voltage differentials similar to the electrical current moving between two battery terminals. When the charged, heated ionic dust struck various mountain sides, flatiron rocks began to form with the cooling and crystallization of the ionic dusts into even almost vertical layers. The triangular formations were created by the dynamic interaction of the winds vibrating and bouncing backward similar to what is seen in wind tunnel experiments.

Part of the physical process was diffusion of the dust materials which created the beautiful multi-colored layers of rock that are parallel to the flatiron surfaces. Diffusion is the kinetic process that leads to the homogenization or uniform mixing of chemical components in a phase. This mixing in a liquid or gas phase occurs on many length scales. When induced by macroscopic flow, diffusive mixing in solids, by contrast, occurs only on the atomic or molecular level. But, as time increases, the length scale can extend to macroscopic distances. A typical 1000 feet of overburden could be scoured easily over extended times.

Further proof of such phenomena is shown to occur on Mars. The atmosphere is 100 times thinner on Mars, 75° C colder, and totally dry. However, Martian dust storms are larger than any observed here on Earth. Occasionally, dust obscures the entire planet. How is this dust transported without the medium of a dense atmosphere? A NASA study of dust devils in the Arizona desert found electric fields more than 10,000 volts per meter. Normal fair-weather electric fields at the Earth's surface measures 100 to 400 volts per meter. Mars has no thunderstorms to release charge into its ionosphere. Electrical energy accumulates between the Martian surface and its ionosphere like a 'planetary capacitor' until the meager atmosphere finally discharges creating whirlwinds or tornadoes of dust moving along the surface and reaching very high into the ionosphere. See "Dust devils on Earth and Mars" by Deborah Byrd in 'Earth' / Sep 18, 2017, found at earthsky.org/earth/dust-devils-earth-mars-5-year-study.

This type of electrical discharge will create fiercer kinetic motions of dust in a thicker, wetter, lowered atmosphere of planet, Earth. The energy stored in Earth's 'planetary capacitor', if certain conditions merged, can easily create horizontal electrical supersonic dust storms that will move many hundreds of feet of sediment, chemically rearrange the atoms, and deposit the material on mountain sides forming flatiron rock cliffs.

There was most likely no surviving witnesses to observe such monstrous turmoil. Any life close to or in the path of this type of electrical storm would be totally obliterated. Humanity can only see its aftermath when viewing such beautifully, naturally formed monuments as these flatiron rocks.

• • •

You have completed a summary and preview of the Great Deluge. Now you should be curious and ready to read the main book and delve into all the details of evidence and logic that supports the cataclysm that ended mankind's Golden Age in the ancient past.

# III.

# INTRODUCTION

The Great Deluge is the story of a huge global flood that caused mass destruction for humanity. However, the story is placed in the file of legends and myths by today's most distant survivors. If it happened, it was a long time ago and could not occur again, unless you are worried about global warming and rising sea level. The story is terrifying and should be well forgotten. The flood story, as will be pointed out, includes other terrifying events that occurred almost simultaneously. Technically, at present, the story is a complete mystery because the water inventory for a fast-global rise in sea level cannot be accounted for. Also, the so-called 40 days and 40 nights of rain in the Noah flood story, if true, is difficult to conceive of, scientifically.

This paper will give accountable reasons for such waters and where they came from and went to. For starters, if the ice sheets of Antarctica fully melted, sea level would rise 60 meters. If Greenland fully melted, there would be a further rise of six meters.[1] That would amount to a total of about 200 feet. But what would cause a sudden rise in days and weeks instead of years and decades, as is anticipated with global warming? The reasons for a sudden rise will be addressed. But first, other major floods throughout man's history will be discussed to eliminate any confusion. The northern hemisphere's glaciation and Antarctica's thicker ice sheets are theorized to have caused a global sea level drop of more than 120 meters (390 feet) over the past 22,000 years.[2] As early man created settlements and small cities, especially close to ocean shorelines, plenty of opportunities arose for major flooding when the ice caps began melting during interglacial warm periods from 22,000 years ago, to the present.

# IV.

# EARLY PRE-DELUGE FLOODING

Much archaeological evidence is available that lists ancient civilizations that were flooded by rising sea level. One of the more famous sites is the Gulf of Cambay in northwestern India. This sunken realm is supposedly part of the Harappan civilization of the Indus Valley that is dated to an unbelievable 9500 years BC, predating the oldest cities in Mesopotamia datable to about 6000 BC. The city is 20 to 40 m (60 to 120 feet) underwater.[3] If this dating is to be trusted, then sea level was 60 to 120 feet lower than today, prior to the Great Deluge event that occurred very close to 9500 BC or 11,500 years BP. Also, Shore Temple Mahabalipujram in eastern India has hidden temples about 80 feet deep under water. The newer temples above water were built about 700 AD.[4]

Off the southern tip of Japan, near Okinawa, is the underwater city of Yonaguni-Jima which is 25 meters (75 feet) deep. Megalithic ruins were discovered near Yucatan Channel off Cuba. The Seahenge of Norfolk England, dated 2100 BC, is built on a tidal flat. See *Sunken Realms – A survey of underwater ruins from around the world* by Karen Mutton for more information.[5]

The Mediterranean Sea has its share of underwater cities. Off Israel's shoreline is Atlit-Yam Haifa, dated to 7000 BC. Near Greece is Pavlopetri Reloponnese that was supposedly engulfed by an earthquake around 1000 BC. Probably the most famous are the ruins of Cleopatra's palace off the shores of Alexandria, Egypt, and the Herakleion and Canopus ruins in the Abu Qir Bay, Egypt. The ruins near Alexandria are thought to be part of the ancient Library of Alexandria and are 20 to 23 feet underwater.[6]

Ancient sea levels fluctuated because of the interspacing of cold periods (glacials) and warm periods (interglacials) but kept rising during the past 20,000 years. Eventually, sea level rose above certain sills at the bottom of passages to other inland seas creating more flooding. The sills for the Dardanelles is 180 feet and for the Bosporus Strait is about 59 feet, which separated the Black Sea from the Mediterranean.[7] Some archaeologists theorize that the Great Deluge was the rapid flooding of the settlements along the Black Sea shoreline. This flooding may or may not have been part of the Great Deluge, depending on whether sea level had already risen to the top of the highest sill of 59 feet depth in the Bosporus Strait.

The connection between the Red Sea and the Indian Ocean is the Bab-el Mandeb Strait, which has an average depth of 609 feet.[8] Very likely, the Red Sea and the ocean were already joined. However, the Strait of Hormuz, between the Persian Gulf and the Indian Ocean, is only 100 to 200 feet deep.[9] The Persian Gulf could have been smaller and its shoreline was either flooded before or during the Great Deluge as sea level rose above the strait's bottom sill. This labeling of normal flooding includes those of the sea level rising in a slower manner from ice sheets melting during various interglacials these past 20,000 years.

What is very clear is that mankind has for many millennia built cities and ports on sea level shorelines with no regard for future sea level rise or fall, as is our present case. If no regard is given to sea level variances, then mankind's civilizations will always be in danger of faltering. However, the Great Deluge, as is being defined by this paper, occurred quickly across the globe and did not afford much warning. Other horrifying events also occurred, causing the Holocene mass extinction event. So, what made the Great Deluge so different from other normal flooding that occurs due to rising rivers and storm surges at sea? The causes of the Great Deluge are forthcoming.

# V.

# POSTULATED GLOBAL SEA AND ICE
# INVENTORIES 20,000 YEARS AGO
# TO THE PRESENT

To make this paper more understandable from the beginning, the sea and ice inventories are postulated at this time. This postulation helps more with sea level and ice sheet fluctuations chronologically rather than with the actual quantities. The best guesstimates and deductions will be tabulated in ice sheet volume correlated to feet of sea level. Three datums are used: the present sea level at zero; the minus 120 ft. level of the Gulf of Cambay site near the Indus River delta dated at 9500 years BC, which was thriving prior to the Great Deluge event; and the lowest theorized sea level of minus 394 ft.[10] The difference in the changing ocean areas between the datums is initially ignored for simplification. This parameter begins to have some significance when seas such as the Black Sea and the Persian Gulf become filled. Also, the ocean crusts, due to the heavier weight of more water, will sink to adjust for isostatic loading. The filling of a larger ocean area and a sinking ocean floor possibly make up for the difference of any additional feet of sea level that are attributed to an assumed thicker East Antarctica ice sheet. Again, I emphasize that the values are somewhat subjective, but based on the best known datums and deductions about ice sheet sizes and sea level fluctuations.

The milestones for major stages are listed. The first is 22,000 to 20,000 years BP when all of Canada and northern United States was covered with the Laurentide ice sheet, all of Greenland was covered by a thicker ice sheet, all of Scandinavia and the extreme western part of Siberia were covered with ice sheets.[11] At that time, East Antarctica was covered by a probably 1.5 to 1.2 times thicker ice sheet (about 200 more meters). A study by the *British Antarctica Survey of Ice Sheets in Antarctica* estimated that, during the Pleistocene, the East Antarctica Ice Sheet thinned by at least 500 meters, with the thinning being less than 50 meters since the Last Glacial Maximum (LGM).[12] This estimation since the last LGM opposes this paper's proposal, since both a substantial change in the Earth's geoid under the ice and the ice thickness made a transition due to slippage of the ice sheet into the ocean. The continental higher mountainous regions, such as the Alps and Himalayas, were completely covered. West Antarctic was considered to have a thinner or no ice sheet at this time due to reasons explained later. The extreme glacial extent for this time is labeled the Last Glacial Maximum (LGM).

The second milestone occurs during the Younger Dryas Period, 12,900 to 11,700 years BP, when the last glacial period ended.[13] The ice sheets prior to and during this geological period covered only half or less of Northern Canada and the entire Greenland region. The Great Lakes region of North America was becoming exposed and creating new lakes and rivers. Just a small portion of the Scandinavian ice sheet still existed.[14] East Antarctica's ice sheet was thinning slightly and West Antarctica's retreating ice sheet exposed a very large percentage of land. This is when sea level had risen from -394 ft. to -120 ft.

The third milestone starts a short time after the Great Deluge event that is hypothesized to have occurred about 11,500 years BP. The Laurentide ice sheet is quickly to moderately decreasing its extent which is already decreased by more than 50% from its original extent. The Greenland ice sheet is still holding, but the Scandinavian ice sheet has disappeared.[15] Most importantly, the East Antarctica ice sheet slides seaward and/or is calving quickly, thereby raising the sea level dramatically. Another phenomenon has occurred with the mid-Atlantic Ocean and mid-Arctic Ocean Rifts; the rifts have opened along most of their length, like a zipper, and released huge reservoirs of hot water, stored under great pressure, into the atmosphere. Severe mud-burdened precipitation of ice and rain form along large storm fronts following global weather patterns. These muddy waters from the so-called *Deep* significantly and temporarily add to sea level height and to layers of sediment on many land masses and ocean bottoms.

The final milestone is the Holocene period, with its present sea level and ice sheets. The Arctic Ocean freezes solid, collecting water as snow. East Antarctic quickly collects snow and ice again to form a new and growing ice sheet and ice shelves in its bays. The West Antarctic ice sheet begins to grow again, too, and becomes covered with ice. Thus, the initial sea level of the Great Deluge drops to the present level slowly over perhaps years and decades, or possibly centuries, but quickly enough so as not to be entirely detected by sea-bed research.

The postulated amounts of ice and sea water are based on relative known areas and thicknesses of major ice sheets throughout the world. Much of the real data for ice sheet sizes is based on ice cores and the amount and velocities of the isostatic adjustments, which is the rise in various land masses due to the disappearance or receding of thick ice sheets. The fluctuations of sea level are based on sea bottom core drillings and general correlations between sea bottom studies and ice cores, tree rings, continental shelf geology, botanical specimens and buried animals. See the predicted ice sheet extents and thickness at various glacial periods on the following Figure 2, Figure 3a[14] and b[15].

## Figure 1. World's Major Ice Sheet Contributions to Sea Level

Measured in Feet After Full Melting

| Years Before Present | Laurentide N. America | Greenland | Scandinavia, W. Siberia and Mtn. Areas | East Antarctica (EAIS) | West Antarctica (WAIS) | Totals |
|---|---|---|---|---|---|---|
| 22,000 to 20,000 BP | -373 ft. | -30 ft. | -20 ft. | -220 ft. | -10 ft. | = 653 ft. |
| (Present ice) → | + 0 | + 20 ft. | + 3 ft. | + 174 ft. | + 16 ft. | = 213 ft. |
| Approximate Global Mean Sea Level is -130 m = -394 ft. 14 m (46 ft.) is added to account for Antarctica's thicker ice in 22,000 BP. The total tally of predicted ice sheet volume is 653 ft. = 394 + 213 + 46. | | | | | | |
| Years Before Present | Laurentide N. America | Greenland | Scandinavia, W. Siberia and Mtn. Areas | East Antarctica (EAIS) | West Antarctica (WAIS) | Totals |
| 11,700 BP (Pre-Deluge) | -156 ft. | - 8 ft. | - 6 ft. | - 209 ft. (1.2 times thicker) | 0 ft. Land mass clear of ice | = 379 ft. |
| Ice melt → | + 217 ft. | + 22 ft. | + 14 ft. | + 11 ft. | + 10 ft. | = 274 ft. |
| Glaciers fluctuated (Laurentide reduced by more than 50%), but generally all ice sheets retreated to create a sea level at -120 feet. | | | | | | |
| 11,500 BP (Post-Deluge) | 0 ft. Moderate melting continues to a full retreat. | -5 ft. Slowly retreats. | -1 ft. Slowly retreats. | -39 ft. | 0 ft. | = 45 ft. |
| Ice melt → | + 217 ft. | + 3 ft. | + 5 ft. | + 170 ft. | 0 ft. | = 395 ft. |

Antarctica's ice sheet slid into ocean to cause a deluge initially of about 170 ft. above present-day sea level. The remaining Laurentide, Greenland and Scandinavian ice sheets continued to melt more slowly or stop, and then eventually the colder climates added to the re-freezing of Greenland's and Antarctica's ice sheets by 168 ft., calculated by subtracting the predicted ice remaining after the deluge from today's current estimates:

$$(20 - 5) + (3 - 1) + (174 - 39) + (16 - 0) = 168 \text{ ft.}$$

| Present Time | 0 ft. | -20 ft. | -3 ft. | - 174 ft. | - 16 ft. | 213 ft. |
|---|---|---|---|---|---|---|

Present sea level if all today's existing major ice sheets melted would rise by about 213 feet.

The tallies for all the world's water, either as water or ice, made equivalent to mean sea level in feet, are listed:
- Complete inventory of ice is represented by the present ice 213 ft. + ice to replace water in oceans from (-394) ft. to present sea level + extra thickness of EAIS of 46 ft. = 653 ft.
- 213 ft. in current ice sheets; present sea level includes the new floating ice of the Arctic Ocean.
- 394 ft. as determined for lowest sea level 20,000 years BP.
- 46 ft. thicker ice sheet is estimated for East Antarctica Ice Sheet which is 1.2 times thicker prior to flood than today.
- A postulated 20 ft. more sea level due to water from the Deep stored under the Earth's hydroplates is initially added to the flood, but is then canceled by the eventual collapse of hydroplate ceilings.

## Figure 2. Laurentide Predicted Ice Sheet Thickness

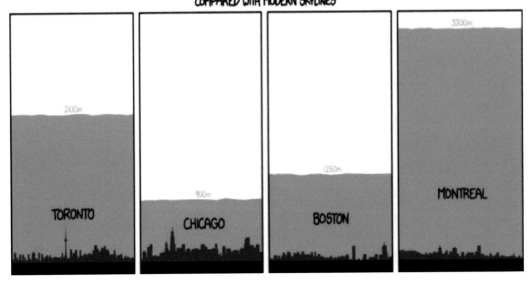

Figure 3a. Predicted Laurentide Ice Sheet Extent:

20,000 (Late Glacial Maximum), 12,900, 11,500 and 8200 years BP

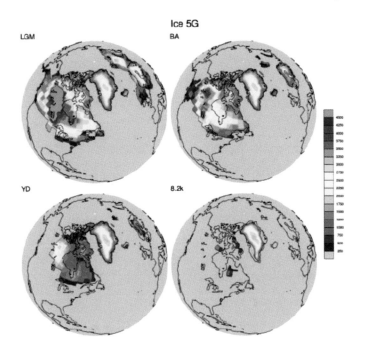

Figure 3b. – Laurentide Ice Sheet Deglaciation at Various Times

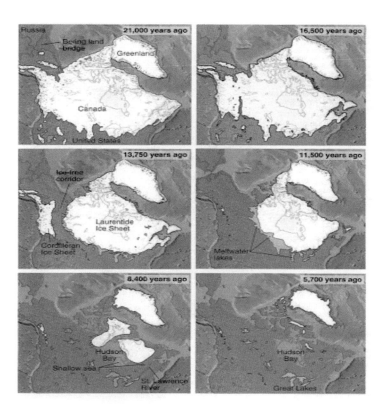

Where did the extra 46 feet of sea water or ice (represented by the pre-deluge thicker EAIS) go? It is presumed to be accounted by a combination of hydroplate collapses, isostatic adjustment of the oceanic crust due to a higher static head of sea water, the increase of water volume as the oceans spread inland and over continental shelves, and the filling of inland seas and river deltas whose connections to the oceans were created as sea level rose. As was previously mentioned, the sills for the straits connecting the Black Sea, at -59 feet, and the Persian Gulf, at -150 to -200 feet, would be flooded at different times; the Black Sea should have been flooded during the Great Deluge and the Persian Gulf during an interglacial ice-sheet melting prior to the Deluge. See the following bar chart of Figure 4: Earth's Total Water Inventory Stored in Ice Sheets and Liquid Oceans During Past Geological Periods for better clarity and understanding.

Important questions that are normally ignored by academia are considered here. Polar ice caps are a planet's coldest regions and are normally located centrally around the poles of the axis of rotation. Why was not all of Siberia covered by ice sheets, since it was as close to the pole as other land masses in North America? Why should the Laurentide ice sheet cover all of southern Canada and most of northern United States, which is much more distant from the North Pole than all of surrounding Siberia? Why should Tasmania and southern New Zealand, in the southern hemisphere, have large ice sheets 20,000 years BP when they are more distant than Western Antarctica and Argentina from the current South Pole?

The answers will be addressed later in more detail when investigating the sudden movement of the Earth's crust and mantle, causing a displacement of polar land masses and the relocating of both geo-magnetic and magnetic poles. This event causes the Antarctica ice sheet to shift into the ocean and suddenly raise sea level. This mantle movement also opened the rifts in the Atlantic and Arctic Oceans, and perhaps other ocean ridges, to create the unprecedented release of hot, pressurized waters and muds high into the atmosphere, which then fell and buried and/or suffocated much flora and fauna in nearby regions.

## Figure 4. Earth's Total Water Inventory Stored in Ice Sheets and Liquid Oceans During Past Geological Periods

Units are in feet of sea level, with respect to present sea level being zero feet;
ice sheet volume is represented by feet of sea level when melted.

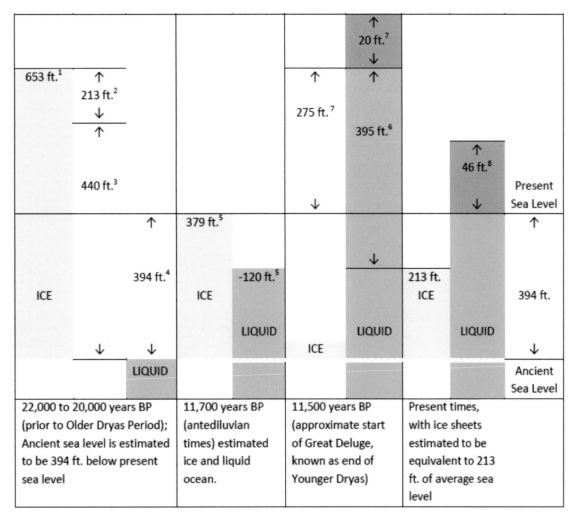

| 22,000 to 20,000 years BP (prior to Older Dryas Period); Ancient sea level is estimated to be 394 ft. below present sea level | 11,700 years BP (antediluvian times) estimated ice and liquid ocean. | 11,500 years BP (approximate start of Great Deluge, known as end of Younger Dryas) | Present times, with ice sheets estimated to be equivalent to 213 ft. of average sea level |

NOTES ON FIGURE 4

[1]   Total ice inventory stored in major ice sheets 20,000 years ago estimated at 653 ft.

[2]   Total present ice inventory stored in ice sheets today is 213 ft.

[3]   Total ice inventory needed to fill oceans to today's sea level is 440 ft., which includes extra ice thickness of East Antarctica Ice Sheet (EAIS) during antediluvian times.

[4]   Lowest sea level during span of 20,000 years ago BP to present is determined to be 394 ft. below present sea level.

[5]   Sea level at -120 ft. from present is determined as the elevation that some civilizations became submerged at about 11,500 years BP; hence, this sea level occurred prior to the Great Flood. The reduced ice inventory at that time was 379 ft. of equivalent sea level: 379 ft. of ice = 653 ft. of ice - (394 ft. - 120 ft.) of water.

[6]   The rise of the "water mountain," or extent of the initial deluge of sea water, is 395 ft. above pre-diluvium sea level at -120 ft. The 395-foot value comes from adding 120 ft. + 275 ft.

[7]   The possible proposed maximum surge of sea water is +275 ft. The release of water reservoirs under the hydroplates (about 20 ft. of equivalent sea level) quickly rose sea level an additional amount, but the hydroplate ceilings eventually collapsed to reclaim that extra water and reduce the longer term maximum extent of ocean waters to +275 ft.; this amount was then reclaimed by the re-freezing of present day ice sheets to achieve present mean sea level at zero feet

[8]   A proposed 46 ft. of depth due to an extra thickness of ice in the EAIS was then reclaimed by filling inland seas and deltas, by covering landmasses along shorelines, by isostatic sinking of crustal oceanic plates due to more hydrostatic head of sea water and by some increase of mountain glaciers. The weight of either additional water or ice on top of the Earth's crust causes it to sink. Even island chains have older sunken volcanoes because the weight of the lava mountain eventually sinks the crust leaving just an atoll.

# VI.

# END OF YOUNGER DRYAS PERIOD–
# THE DEFINING MOMENT

The Younger Dryas event is an anomalous, striking geological period occurring 12,900 to 11,700 years BP according to the calibrated radiocarbon and other isotope-ratio dating methods.[16] The various dating methods have a fairly high range of variability and/or inaccuracy with some different types of data conflicting each other. More details of these dating methods and their assumptions will be discussed later. However, keep in mind that if a major catastrophe occurred on Earth during this time, it had to actually occur over days, perhaps weeks, months or years, but certainly not hundreds of years. Some of the dating data does reveal that the Earth's recovery from this event took over hundreds of years by adjustments to the geoid, sea level fluctuations, changes to atmospheric conditions and regional climates, the melting of current ice sheets and build-up of new ice sheets and sea ice.

## A. EFFECT OF INCREASED SOLAR WINDS

Let's summarize all the stages in this Great Deluge event. The first thing to occur was the appearance of an alien sky that portrayed unusual electrical plasma displays. A celestial intruder was about to enter the inner solar system. Very possibly, this intruder was a brown dwarf star system with its own planets. As this system nears our Sun's system, their individual magnetospheres clash and create very unusual displays of plasma glow discharges and currents. Also, the Sun begins to discharge more than the average amount of charged particles into its solar wind which reach the planets, including Earth. Fantastic auroras are created as both positive and negative charges fall onto the Earth's polar regions. These particles travel from the poles toward the equator creating huge currents in the conductive moist atmosphere and salty oceans which induces a highly-magnetized crust and mantle, adding to the already magnetized Earth due to the dynamo effects of the inner iron core. This surge of particles moving along the Earth's surface also creates sudden climatic changes and severe storms.

## B. HIGH ENERGY PLASMA DISCHARGE FROM A CLOSE ENCOUNTER

As the brown dwarf system enters between Mars and Jupiter on a particularly close perihelion, one of its own highly cathodic, negatively charged, magnetized planets is perturbed by the Sun's planets. It has a very rare close encounter with Earth. For Earth's inhabitants, this celestial body looks very much like a giant comet with tails spreading over large portions of the sky. The tails are being created by the overly active solar wind of the Sun interacting with the rogue planet's own magnetosphere. As the close encounter comes closer, the more highly and overly charged rogue planet discharges high energy plasma directly upon the north polar region of Earth. These discharges then travel, like horizontal lightning bolts, through the rivers, oceans and atmosphere toward the equator from both poles, but mostly from the North Pole as it is closest to the rogue intruder. This flow of current on the rotating Earth further magnetizes the crust and deeply embeds itself into the mantle.

## C. MAGNETIC FIELDS INTERACT

At closest approach, the rogue planet and Earth act like large magnets interacting with each other, like what happens when one passes a bar magnet near another to slightly rotate the other, but not close enough so as to come together. However, the Earth has too much mass and angular momentum to be tilted. The Earth's massive core and mantle act like a gyroscope which stabilizes its axis of tilt. The crust and mantle with about 67% of the overall mass have become recently more magnetized and rotate as one unit on the liquid iron core by 20 to 30 degrees of latitude. The accumulated pull force of the rogue planet's magnetic field yanks this spherical globe of crust and mantle along a meridian line that closely goes through the center of North and South America, East Antarctica and then western China.

Figure 5. Temperatures and Depths of Crust-to-Mantle and
Mantle-to-Outer Liquid Core Interfaces that Act Like Liquid Clutches

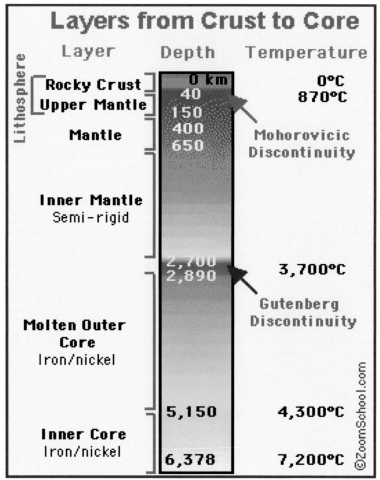

Credit: Enchanted Learning Image

Figure 6. The Earth's Internal Heat, Due to Increasing Pressure,
Creates Sliding Layers Between the Crust and Mantle, Called the Moho
Discontinuity, and Between the Solid Mantle and Liquid Outer Core

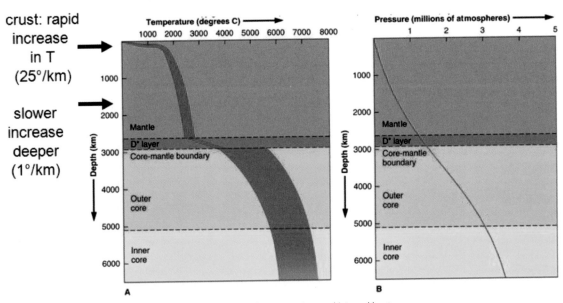

Credit: SlidePlayer; Isostasy, gravity, magnetism and internal heat

## D. EARTH'S GEOID IS CHANGED

Planet Earth's geoid has a natural oblate spherical shape as shown in the following figure. This shape is due to the centripetal forces being stronger at the equator than at the polar regions because the surface velocities are higher. These forces pull the Earth's crust outward about 6 miles farther on its radius than at the poles. This difference in elevation is significant for standing bodies of water on top of the crust, which may run off to lower elevations if the geoid changes enough at their locations. If the crust and mantle are rotated differently with respect to the spin axis, then globally the crust is disturbed enough that fissures open to allow subterranean magma reservoirs to release their pressure and create new volcanoes or activate existing ones. Because the crust either raises or lowers, earthquakes ensue and the edges of tectonic plates are shoved under or over each other. Crusts in some mountainous region can be squeezed laterally to create accordion-like structures in sedimentary rocks. Sudden uplifts of mountain ranges and sinking plateaus are also created. For the entire crust and mantle to be displaced as a single unit by 30 degrees latitudinally, upward or downward movements of the crust can be as much as 2 miles in elevation.

The geoid of the Earth changes in some places more slowly than others, but nevertheless, the resettling of the geoid caused by the centripetal force of the spinning Earth[17] causes earthquakes and volcanism on a global scale. The run-away volcanism places more carbon dioxide and dust into the atmosphere, blocking out the warmth of the Sun in many regions for long periods of time. In addition, ridges or rifts on the oceanic bedrock opens and releases large amounts of highly pressurized water held under hydroplates, or what is known as the supported oceanic plates. The released water rises high into the atmosphere to cause many continuing days of precipitation and wet dust fall that become cemented together in the appearance of layers over numerous landscapes. The forces of magnetism of the passing rogue planet are greatest over the north polar region; hence, the initial tug on the crust and upper mantle severely pulls open the existing rift under the Arctic Ocean. The almost immediate release of high-pressure water under the hydroplates causes a surge of hot water and liquid rock to be ejected high into the upper atmosphere, where it is cooled rapidly and then falls back as sleet, hail and muck on the surrounding regions of Alaska, Canada and Siberia, causing the pasturing megafauna in these regions to suffocate and/or be buried alive. Many mammoths are reported to have been found buried in a standing position due to the intensity of mud or loess falling from the sky.

### Figure 7. An Exaggerated Oblate Spheroidal Earth

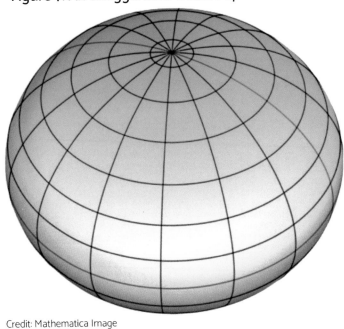

Credit: Mathematica Image

### Figure 8. Earth's Oblateness to Scale

The dark blue line represents an ellipse with the same eccentricity as that of the Earth with north on top. The yellow area denotes the range of the International Space Station.

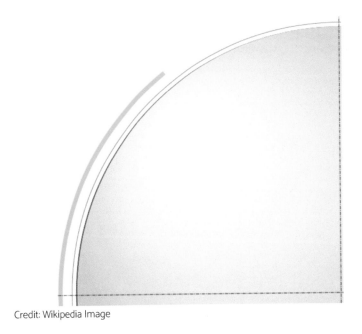

Credit: Wikipedia Image

## Figure 9. World Map Showing How Crust/Mantle Shifted Latitudinally 30° from a Predicted Antediluvian North Pole Centered in Hudson Bay

Southward along a 75° West Meridian Line in the Western Hemisphere and Northward along a 105° Meridian Line in the Eastern Hemisphere

## Figure 10. World's Tectonic Plates Showing Approximate Antediluvian Equator with Its North Pole Located Just South of the Hudson Bay

The geoid adjustment lifts the crustal plates in some places and depresses them in other regions; Africa and the mid-Pacific probably received minor elevation changes.

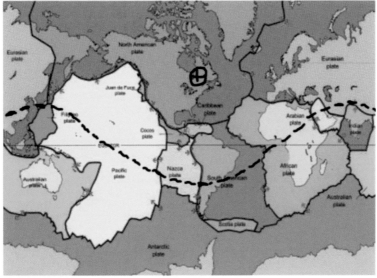

Credit: Wikipedia Image

## E. POLAR ICE SHEETS DISPLACED FROM THE POLAR SPIN AXIS

The major ice sheets near the poles were displaced by 20 to 30 degrees of latitude causing the rapid melting of the remaining Laurentide, Greenland and Scandinavian ice sheets, thereby creating an accelerated freshwater flux into the oceans. Although many ice sheets were now melting, due to being displaced by more than 20 degrees of latitude to the south, general atmospheric temperature was dropping rapidly, due to ocean waters' receiving unprecedented amount of ice from tidal water calving, the fierce changes in climatic winds and the atmosphere's being infused by large amounts of dust and water coming from both the hydroplates and increased volcanism. The Sun's radiant heat energy was severely blocked, causing a rapid atmospheric cool-down in spite of the tidal glaciers' accelerating their calving into the sea. This immense and almost immediate cool-down is represented in error as the beginning of the Younger Dryas period starting at 12,900 years BP. This error will be explained later.

### Figure 11. The Major North American Ice Sheets are Centrally Located about the Southern End of the Hudson Bay Area where the Antediluvian North Pole Existed

It is assumed that the Arctic Ocean was not frozen at this time; the overall colder world climate and local cold winds and ocean currents are assumed to have caused the West Canadian Cordilleran and the Scandinavian Ice Sheets.

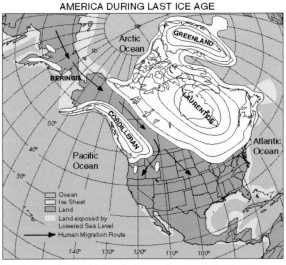

Credit: Emporia State University Image; America during last ice age

### Figure 12. Maximum Extent of Scandinavian, British Isles and Western Siberian Ice Sheets about 20,000 Year BP

Their extent was much less just prior to the Great Deluge.

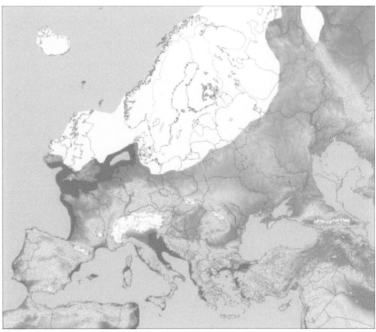

Credit: Pinterest Image; Europe during last glacial period

## F. SLIDING OF ANTARCTICA ICE SHEET AND SUDDEN RISE IN SEA LEVEL

Surely, for the inhabitants of Earth, the situation could not possibly worsen, but it did. Because the Earth was in a period of glaciation, the Antarctica ice sheet was thicker by an estimated 1.2 to 1.5 times. The subsequent isostatic loading sank the bedrock but not far enough to be below sea level. However, the thicker ice sheet produced pressures high enough to create a phase change of liquid water and produce slush above the bedrock. But enough contact points between the blue ice and bed rock produced stability. When the southern ice cap was displaced by 20 to 30 degrees, the Earth's polar axis was now placed squarely toward the center of the continent and was no longer on the edge of East Antarctica or in the adjacent Southern Ocean. The geoid, in reaching equilibrium closer to the pole, allowed the bedrock to move downward to where the liquid water and slush boundary were at or below sea level. The reduced centripetal forces of the spinning geoid on East Antarctica were reduced enough to allow this crustal region to sink even more under the weight of ice. Now the Southern Ocean could aid, by seepage and buoyancy, to lift huge portions of the East Antarctica's ice sheet and slide them completely into the ocean, thereby raising sea level significantly. The sliding motion, of course, was initiated by the movement of the crust in the opposite direction, thereby causing a reaction of the heavy ice sheet to move in the other direction, toward the ocean. The slippery surface of the slushy under-bottom made the movement much easier.

This rise in sea level due to the Antarctica ice sheet would eventually flood all of man's existing ocean ports and shore settlements – probably not by tsunami waves, but by a slow continuingly rise similar to low tide going to high tide, but never ceasing to keep rising. The continuing rise would eventually flood inland seas, if not already flooded, like the Black Sea, and further flood the Persian Gulf after ocean connections were made through their straits. This relentless inundation of sea water, without warning, could easily wipe out the more important population centers clustered in lowlands near the oceans and seas. The following chart indicates the location of East Antarctica's ice sheet bottom, the slush region and top of landmass, with respect to the quickly rising sea level in those times. The reasons are now very clear why such an ice sheet can calve or break away and slide into the sea.

**Figure 13. Composite Satellite Photography of West Antarctic left of the Main Mountain Range and East Antarctica right of the Same Mountains**

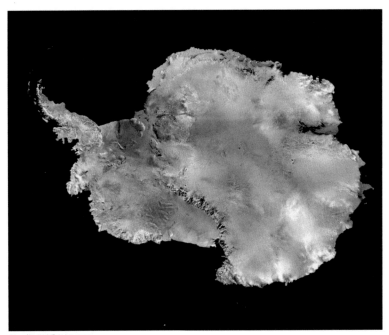

Credit: NASA Image

## Figure 14: Charting the Reasons for East Antarctica Ice Sheet (EAIS) at the Highest Elevations Sliding into the Ocean
### (Chart 1)

Units are in feet of approximate ice thickness or landmass elevation either above or below present average sea level at zero feet.

| Scale | | | | |
|---|---|---|---|---|
| 16,000' | | | | 15,700[22] ↑ ↑ |
| | 15,070[6] ↑ ↑ | ↑ | | ↑ ↑ |
| | ↑ ↑ | | | |
| | | 5280[11] | | New ice 7360[13] |
| | Ice sheet | | | |
| | prior to 10,500[5] | ↓ | | ↓ |
| 10,000' | Flood | 9790[7] ↑ ↑ | 9790 ↑ | ↓ 10,500 |
| | | ↑ ↑ | ↑ | 8340[12] ↑ |
| | | | | old ice ↑ |
| | 18,840[1] | | | |
| | Slush line ↓ | Ice sheet | | 5200[26] 8340[12] ↓ |
| 5000' | xxxxxxxxxx ↓ | after bed- | ice that | xxxxxxxxxx ↓ |
| | 4570[2] | rock sank 10,500 | slid into 10,500 | ↓ |
| | | | ocean | 2800 ↓ |
| | | 18,840 | | ///////// ↑ |
| | | | +170[20] ↑ | 2800[19] ↓ |
| 0' | ^^^^^^^^^ ←Present S.L. | ^^^^^^^^^ | ^^^^^^^^^ | ^^^^^^^^^ |
| | ********* ←Ancient S.L. | ********* ←-120[4] | ********* 880[10] | |
| | | -710[8] ↓ | -710 ↓ | |
| | ↓ | xxxxxxxxxx ↓ | xxxxxxxxxx ↓ ↓ | |
| | -3770[3] ↓ | | ↑ | Land mass |
| | ///////// ←bedrock ↑ | | Old ice ↑ | raises |
| -5000' | ↑ | | | after ice |
| | Sank 5280' | | 8340[12] | slides into |
| | due to geoid | | | ocean |
| | ↓ | ↓ | ↓ | |
| | ↓ | -9050[9] ↓ | -9050 ↓ | |
| -10,000' | | ///////// | ///////// | |
| Scale | Predicted antediluvian EAIS with the highest elevations. | Earth's geoid is adjusting downward during the deluge event's process of mantle shifting for Antarctica's highest elevations. | For thicker regions, the top of ice sheet above slush line slid or calved into ocean, leaving older ices below the slush line. | Present highest and thickest ice of EAIS. |

## Figure 15. Charting the Reasons for East Antarctica Ice Sheet (EAIS) at *Average Elevations* Sliding into the Ocean
## (Chart 2)

Units are in feet of approximate ice thickness or landmass elevation either above or below present average sea level at zero feet.

| | | | | |
|---|---|---|---|---|
| 15,000' | | | | |
| | 12,830[16] ↑ | | | |
| | ↑ | ↑ | | |
| 10,000' | 9770[17] ↑ | 5280 | | 9000[25] ↑ |
| | 10,500[5] ↑ | | | ↑ |
| | for slush | ↓ | | |
| | | 7550[19] | 7550 | 6200[24] |
| | If 7440[18] | | New ice | |
| 5000' | no slush | | Ice that | |
| | forms | | slid into | ↓ |
| | 2330[14] ↓ ↓ | | ocean | ///////// ↑ |
| | XXXXXXXXXXX ↓ ↓ | | | 2800 2800[23] |
| | ///////// ↑ | | +170[20] ↑ ↑ | ↓ |
| 0' | ^^^^^^^^^ Present S.L. | ^^^^^^^^^ | ^^^^^^^^^ 290[20] | ^^^^^^^^ |
| | ********* Ancient S.L. | ********* ←-120[4] | ********* ↓ | Land mass |
| | 5280[11] | -2950[15] | -2950  3120[21] | rises |
| | ↓ | XXXXXXXXX | XXXXXXXXXX ↓ | after ice |
| | | ///////// | ///////// | slides into |
| -5000' | | | | ocean |
| Scale | Predicted antediluvian EAIS with average ice sheet thickness adjusted for isostatic load of increased glaciation. | For much of the ice average thickness, the slush line was near the top of the land mass or did not exist before geoid adjustments sank the crust and bedrock. | Landmass with or without slush boundary sinks below antediluvian sea level of about -120 feet for the average ice sheet thickness. The ice either slides into ocean or is lifted off the land by buoyancy. | Present average thickness of ice and landmass elevation of EAIS. The EAIS recovered to present day conditions. New ice and snow collected on the land mass after the bedrock rebounded and rose to elevations about 2800 feet above the current sea level where current equilibrium is attained. |

Symbols:

Predicted Ice Sheet Thickness that always stayed with the landmass - [ ]

Part of ice sheet that slid into the ocean - [ ]

Normal Ice Sheet Thickness - [ ]

Landmass Surface and Top – [ ///////// ]

Current sea level - ^^^^^^^

Antediluvian and postdiluvian sea levels - ********

Slush line created by pressurized ice - xxxxxxxx

## NOTES ON FIGURES 14 AND 15

[1]     18,840 ft. is the predicted thickest ice sheets near mountain ridges and high plateaus based on (1.2 x 15,700 ft.); 15,700 ft. is the published current thickest and deepest ice in the EAIS.[18] The factor of 1.2 discussed previously is used for the increase in glaciation from the present immediately prior to the Great Deluge event.

[2]     4570 ft. = (15,070 ft. – 10,500 ft.) is the predicted highest slush line elevation where water achieves a pressurized melting point near a range centered at about a depth of 10,500 ft. of ice.[19]

[3]     Negative 3770 ft. = -(18,840 ft. x 0.2) = the estimated average bedrock elevation for higher elevations in the EAIS; the multiplier of 0.2 is the isostatic adjustment, or sinking, of landmass elevation based on factoring the thickness of ice today with the thicker ice of antediluvian times.

[4]     Negative 120 ft. is the postulated antediluvian sea level, as previously discussed.

[5]     10,500 ft. is the published depth of ice and snow where its resulting hydrostatic weight with its combined pressure and temperature creates water.[19] This demarcation where phase of water is briefly changed to liquid from ice shall be called the "slush line or boundary".

[6]     15,070 = 18,840 – 3770 = elevation of the top of the ice sheet after the isostatic adjustment or sinking of the average landmass surface of 3770 feet is subtracted.

[7]     9790 = 15070 -5280 = changed top of ice sheet after adjustment of the Earth's geoid that sinks the crust a further 5280 feet.

[8]     Negative 710 ft. = 9790 ft. – 10,500 ft. = the changed slush line elevation which is now well below the antediluvian sea level of -120 feet.

[9]     Negative 9050 ft. =-3770 ft. – 5280 = the new elevation of the sinking bedrock.

[10]    880 ft. = + 170 ft. sea level + elevation of slush line at minus 710 ft. equals the elevation differential available for the sea water to lift off the buoyant ice sheet from the landmass.

[11]    The oblate Earth produces a difference of approximately 6 miles on radius at the equator x 30/90 degrees of latitude = 1/3 x 6 miles = 2 miles. A conservative amount of adjustment or change in oblateness under the EAIS is chosen as one mile, or **5280 ft.** This hypothetical geoid adjustment is not perfect at the polar regions and should have some amount of delay function.

[12]    8340 ft. = 9050 ft. – 710 ft. = postulated thickness of old blue ice left on the landmass after isostatic adjustments raised the continents surface due to no ice load immediately after the Great Deluge Event. If the ice cores measured ices older than 11,500 years, then very possibly these older ices were part of the core's specimen. The better-known ice cores of the EAIS were taken well-inland near the ice divides, where older antediluvian ice still existed. Ice core specimens have difficulty recognizing a steady aging process of the core past 8500 years ago because the layers are no longer visible after being squashed horizontally into one volume of blue ice.

[13]    7360 ft. = 15,700 ft. – 8340 ft. = postulated thickness of new ice added to ice sheet after Earth recovered from the Great Deluge.

[14]    2330 ft. = 2800 ft. / 1.2 = the pre-deluge elevation of the average bedrock and/or the slush line for most of the East Antarctica Ice Sheet accounting for the isostatic adjustment due to estimating 1.2 times thicker ice sheet.

[15]    Negative 2950 ft. = (2330 ft. -5280 ft.) below present sea level is the location of the slush boundary that is sitting on the landmass, which is now well under the antediluvian sea level. Now the oceans provide buoyancy to lift and/or slide large portions of the ice sheet off the landmass and into the ocean to become giant floating ice shelves. The immense volume of ice now raises ocean levels on a global scale.

[16]    12,830 ft. = 10,500 ft. + 2330 ft. = the top of the ice sheet if a slush boundary is achieved near the top of the bedrock. In this case, the ice sheet will be 1.4 times thicker than present conditions.

[17]    9770 ft. = 7440 ft. + 2330 ft. = the top of the ice sheet if the ice sheet is 1.2 times thicker than present conditions. For this case, theoretically no slush boundary would exist.

[18]   7440 ft. = 1.2 x 6200 ft. = the increase in ice sheet thickness due to the projected increase of glaciation during antediluvian times with no regard to a slush boundary occurring.

[19]   7550 ft. = 12,830ft. – 5280 ft. = the top of the ice sheet at average elevations after the bedrock sank in these regions by about 5280 ft.

[20]   290 ft. = 120 ft. + 170 ft. = the total rise in sea level from its antediluvian level of -120 ft. from present sea level, producing a total swell of 290 ft. for the inhabitants of Earth at that time. The 170-ft. rise above present sea level is taken from the analysis in the table of Figure 1 World's Major Ice Sheet Contributions to Sea Level. Due to the interval of time it took for the total affected ice sheet to leave the landmass by sliding and calving, most likely, a steadier rise in sea level took place instead of a series of tsunamis.

[21]   3120 ft. = 170 ft. + 2950 ft. = the average depth of bedrock and bottom of the ice sheet under the flooded seas. Plenty of buoyancy is available to lift off the ice sheet from the land mass.

[22]   15,700 ft. is the published maximum thickness of ice of the EAIS.[18] Mid-continental mountain ridges rise above the ice sheet with higher elevations. All of EAIS rests on bedrock above sea level, unlike West Antarctica's Ice Sheet which is mostly below sea level. The WAIS is presently considered to be unstable. During antediluvian times, West Antarctica was probably mostly lowlands, with little ice sheet formation. After the Deluge event, West Antarctica gained a sizable ice sheet that sank the landmass, due to isostatic adjustments.

[23]   2800 ft. is the published average bedrock elevation of ice of the EAIS.[19] Most of the area of EAIS is around this elevation as one moves quickly away from the ice divides and mountain ridges that divide West and East Antarctica.

[24]   6200 ft. is the published average ice thickness of the EAIS, which is away from the mountain ridges separating East and West Antarctica.[20]

[25]   9000 ft. = (6200 ft. + 2800 ft.) is simply the average elevation of the EAIS when adding the average ice thickness and average bedrock elevation together.[19, 20]

[26]   5200 ft. = (15,700 ft. – 10,500 ft.) is the expected elevation for finding the present slush line and sub-glacial liquid lakes in the deepest ices and/or troughs of the EAIS.[19]

# G. HOLOCENE MASS EXTINCTION EVENT

The result of just not flooding, but all the other attendant catastrophes, created the Holocene mass extinction event. The Clovis people of North America were totally wiped out, due to living close to the meridian where all the electromagnetic forces and plasma discharges from the rogue planet were directed and concentrated. These peoples were either burned or electrocuted or covered by volcanic ash. For any existing developed civilizations throughout the world, their infrastructure would be mostly, if not completely, destroyed. Most importantly, complete annihilation is certain for the more intelligent, aggressive peoples living along shorelines and other waterways, where the most destruction would occur. The survivors would have lost the talents and memories of their ancient intelligentsia and be driven back to the Stone Age. Survival was critical, with only meager tools and a destroyed infrastructure for living in these harsh conditions of colder climates and a fouled land surface and atmosphere.

This grand postulation of catastrophic events occurred about 11,500 years BP according the modern dating methods. The boundary of large concentrated groupings of sudden destruction of flora and fauna occurs during or near the end of the Younger Dryas geological period. This author believes that other dated parameters of these times such as freshwater influx, accumulation of snow on ice sheets and temperature fluctuations indicate a definite beginning of the Younger Dryas of 12,900 years BP (from the Greenland ice core GRIP) marking the pending cataclysm.[26] This point in time must include the cited inaccuracies and conflicting dates of ±150 years for the various dating methods. Larger, very possible inaccuracies, due to so-called calibrated constants really become suspect and too variable under the previously mentioned chaotic effects of the Earth's surface during this cataclysm. The author seriously questions whether various dating methods, especially that of radiocarbon dating, can realistically make very close predictions of these turbulent times within even ±1000 years.

## H. ASTROBLEMES OF THE NORTH POLAR REGION

The Hudson Bay, and its adjoining, smaller James Bay are postulated to be astroblemes created during this event. The word *astrobleme* is used to identify an impact crater on Earth that has been almost hidden by erosion and water. Although thought to be very ancient meteorite impacts, these astroblemes were created by the giant electrical discharges directly connecting a column of plasma between the Earth's magnetic North Pole of those times with the closely passing rogue planet. The material from these astroblemes was sputtered and ejected high into the atmosphere, just as material is sputtered in industrial electrical arc cutting. More than likely, the present erratic boulders randomly resting unexplainably on the northern-latitude land masses were sputtered from the Hudson-Bay and James Bay astroblemes.

James Bay was caused by one of the major leading, subordinate, off-centered discharges. The materials scoured from this smaller astrobleme probably caused the bombardment of the *Carolina Bays*, an intriguing topographical phenomenon.[21] There are hundreds of thousands of these "bays" lying clearly visible and scattered across the Atlantic Coastal Plain from Maryland to northern Florida. These so-called bays are shallow depressions averaging 500 feet long and only known of recently by using aerial photography. They vary by size and shape, but most are elliptical, parallel to each other and oriented in the same direction from north-west to south-east, especially in the Carolinas. Strangely and coincidently enough, when looking on a globe, these elliptical and ovate shapes in the Carolinas align with the longer shape of James Bay in Canada. More examples of this same type of concentrations with oriented shallow depressions (sometimes as lakes) exist in Nebraska, Alaska, northern

Canada, Bolivia and Siberia. There is a question that these bays have some type of celestial origin; the lack of meteorites found in these locations leads one inductively to a bombardment of both rock and large chunks of ice coming from Earth's own astroblemes caused by immense electrical discharge and sputtering of surface rock and chunks of ice sheets.

# VII.

# ANSWERS TO THE CONTROVERSIES AND TECHNICAL OBJECTIONS OF THE DELUGE PROPOSAL

## A. CELESTIAL INTRUDER

One of the biggest objections to the previous hypothesis is that a celestial intruder passes through or is captured by the solar system. Suspicion arises due to knowing that the closest known objects are star systems about four light years away. However, even the "top gun" scientists of NASA have developed an ad hoc scheme for a rogue planet glancing off Earth and slowing sufficiently to be captured and orbit Earth as our Moon. This theory is much more acceptable, in that it supposedly occurred more than four billion years ago and not just 11,500 years BP. The current scientific community fully accepts uniformitarianism as nature's methodology except during the time closest to the creation of the solar system about 4.6 billion years ago. A recent catastrophic event such as the Great Deluge is still not in the playbook of consensus science. The current paradigm is that any drastic changes occurring to our so-called stable solar system occurred only very early, when stars and the Sun were formed in a crowded nursery, allowing for star systems to interact momentarily and throw planets at each other. Of course, the major extinction events occurring about every 26 million years are still being scrutinized but less so due to the lack of any model that provides a long periodic celestial intruder.

## 1. The Captured Proto-Planet, Saturn

This discussion of high energy arcing between celestial bodies leads us directly to *The Electric Universe*, by Wallace Thornhill and David Talbott[22] who perfected this theory of electrical discharges between celestial bodies. These authors are proponents of the *electric universe* (EU), in claiming that electromagnetic (EM) energy shapes and controls the universe, its galaxies, stars and planets. This is in direct opposition to the accepted dogma of gravity being the magic wand of creation. They, and their online

Thunderboltsproject.com, have made a believer of me. Their arguments and proposals are extremely convincing, except for one main issue. This *Electric Universe* (EU) group does not yet accept the intervening orbiting brown dwarf hypothesis. This group, of course, utilizes an intruder to the solar system, which is the planet Saturn, that was recently captured. Saturn was originally a brown dwarf that became a proto-planet. The planet, in attempting to reach electrical equilibrium, eventually ejected the planets of Mars, Earth and Venus from its polar region. This part of their hypothesis called the *polar configuration* is difficult to swallow; nevertheless, I am very impressed with their other ideas and am in almost complete agreement with their other EU hypotheses. More about their ideas of electricity in space will be presented later.

## 2. The Phaeton Hypothesis

Co-authors D. Allan and J. Delair, introduced an intruder they called *Phaeton* in their very instructive and informative book, *Cataclysm, Compelling Evidence of a Cosmic Catastrophe in 9500 B.C.*[23] The book is a scholarly work professing that the Great Deluge events indeed occurred. Much evidence utilizing botanical, zoological, geological and geophysical data is presented. Unfortunately, these trained geologists tried to pin this tragedy on the close encounter of a rogue celestial body coming from the Vega star system and acting like a large comet when entering the Sun's system of planets. Their diagram shows this celestial body making one pass through the planetary system, having close encounters with Pluto, Neptune, Uranus, Saturn, a planet called Tiamat, Mars, Earth and Venus before crashing into the Sun. This scenario is absolutely impossible, and henceforth, these authors lost their credibility at trying to be astrophysicists. This subject was not their forte. Many of their better ideas are used in this current postulation. Their book will be discussed later in more detail.

## 3. Orbiting Brown Dwarf Star System

I am hoping that this paper's rogue planetary intruder coming from a brown dwarf star makes more sense to the astrophysical community, even though they will probably still inconvincibly disagree. The brown dwarf star is clothed in a darkened plasma glow, similar to a red giant star, but much dimmer and smaller, which makes it difficult to detect throughout the entire electromagnetic spectrum. This sister star to our Sun has its own planets and orbits an estimated 3600 years around the Sun. Its varying perihelion passes between the orbits of Mars and Jupiter. On each orbital pass, different scenarios occur, depending on the locations of planets and the varying charged densities of the two stars and their individual planets. Sometimes, there are close encounters between planets, such as happened with Earth 11,500 years ago. There is an ongoing search for this Planet-X, or Nemesis, or this brown dwarf star, in the southern hemisphere. This author's calculations have determined that the brown dwarf system passed through three more times since 11,500 BP, with certain recorded chaos each time but less severe than the Great Deluge event. The brown dwarf is predicted to be currently traveling toward its aphelion and will not return until about 4900 A.D. The star and its planets are highly electrical in nature and when they clash with either the Sun's heliopause or the Sun's planets' magnetopauses, high energy glowing plasma discharges are created. These glowing Birkland currents become visible to inhabitants on Earth as the brown dwarf system approaches the inner solar system. If then a rare, but inevitable, close encounter occurs between two celestial bodies, a very high energy plasma discharge can occur between them, looking like a giant lightning bolt. The evidence is made very clear that this electrical energy exchange can and does exist, as is seen with Valles Marinaris on Mars, with its deep 3000-mile gouge and dendritic valleys. Only an immense plasma arc could have produced this geological wonder.

## 4. Competing Ideas

In summary, one can now appreciate the competing ideas for chaos-creating intruders to our so-called serene and stable solar system. NASA has the "Giant Impact Hypothesis" for creating Earth's Moon[24] and is slowly considering a possible celestial encounter, such as a huge comet, to create the disturbance for the Holocene extinction event. D. Allan and J. Delair in *Cataclysm* believe that an extra-solar planet-like body cruised through the solar system, making numerous close encounters, and then crashed into the Sun. This scenario is virtually impossible from either a gravitational or EM viewpoint. Thornhill and Talbott have proposed very intriguing and excellent ideas, such as the giant outer planets being captured brown dwarfs, then, these proto-planets eject binary bodies that then orbit their equators due to EM imbalances. However, these authors are trapped in their own paradigm, presenting in their thunderbolts.info the preposterous theory of the Saturn polar configuration and that the inner planets are ejected from Saturn's pole within man's life-time, which hurts their overall credibility. Please understand that this indictment is totally this author's judgment based on my not-so-perfect understanding of the laws of physics. And finally, the continuing orbiting brown dwarf sister star, with its own planets, is on top of the list for the competing hypotheses for the cause of the Great Deluge. This same idea can also dovetail into a reason for the creation of the Earth-Moon system, which NASA desperately desires. See ettingerjournals.com/dbe_ mankind.shtml "A Brief History of Mankind's Chaotic Past" for more information about the history of the Sun's sister star.

## B. CRUST AND MANTLE DISPLACEMENT

Another large technical objection to this Great Deluge hypothesis is inevitable. How is it possible to rotate the crust and mantle together as one unit by 20 to 30 degrees of latitude? Naturally, if the crust is proven to be displaced, then the mantle underneath has to move in an almost corresponding manner. The entire mantle can possibly move as one piece, since it sits on a liquid iron core that is coupled electrically and magnetically to the mantle. If some event momentarily and electrically de-couples this liquid/magnetic clutch-like surface, and simultaneously some large enough exterior force yanks the outer mantle, then mantle displacement is entirely possible. Of course, the exterior force would need to be large enough to overcome the stored angular momentum within the mantle. One must think of two gyroscopes – one inside the other – that are loosely connected and have identical orientation of spin axes. Then, the outer gyroscope becomes very magnetized and is briefly disturbed by an external magnet, a brown dwarf star or one of its planets, to push it sideways. Simultaneously, the interface between the two gyroscopes is de-coupled electrically and magnetically to allow some movement of the outer gyroscope's axis by 30 degrees, before becoming coupled again to the inner gyroscope. This scenario is comparable to pushing a spinning top horizontally from its top pole and making it wobble. Pushing the spinning top horizontally near its center is almost impossible to make it wobble. The top may be slowed, but not tilted, in this case.

Due to the abrupt change in spin axis vector of the mantle, horizontal forces are created on the crust, which cause local slipping of major tectonic plates with respect to the upper mantle. The plates push against each other at their edges, creating land uplift and new or higher mountain ranges. The movement of the tectonic plates is made easier because the mantle and crust interface is heated and mobile. This interface, called the Moho layer, becomes less viscous due to the electrical heating from the polar region's arc discharges and subsequent high energy current flow through the crustal surface. The granitic, lighter continental plates, moving westward in the American continents, ride over top the heavier oceanic plates, to create the uplifting of the Andes, Sierra, Cascade and Rocky Mountain Ranges. The oceanic plates, moving westward toward Asia, ride under the lighter continental Asian plates to create both mountain and island chain building and deep ocean trenches.

## 1.  Earth's Crust and Mantle Become Strongly Magnetized

This scenario as just explained is what happened. The close encounter created an exchange of charged particles via an immense thunderbolt or high energy plasma discharge between the bodies of Earth and another closely passing charged body. The charged particles, mostly electrons, created currents that spread fairly evenly around the surface of the spinning Earth. This EM circuitry induced magnetized top layers of the mantle and weakened the electrical coupling between the mantle and the inner liquid core. Then, the resulting magnetic forces between the stronger magnetism of the passing rogue body, displaced the entire magnetized mantle during a very short period when the bodies were at closest approach. As this rogue intruder moved past, the magnetic force on the mantle ceased and the inner core coupled again after the mantle was displaced in a certain direction, similar to one bar magnet's passing another to partially rotate it.

NASA scientists and university researchers need to recognize such a scenario and test it with computerized models. What amount of magnetism on Earth can be created by an electrical current being received near the north pole? Is the magnetic force required to briefly change the angular momentum of the mantle reasonable? This author's capabilities are limited, especially not having direct connections with any university faculty and little knowledge of creating computer models. More convincing of academia is required for them to move forward with the required computer analyses. Therefore, I now present what I consider is direct proof that this scenario occurred.

## 2. Convincing Indications for Displaced Mantle

Firstly, it is obvious that the polar regions, as defined by the ice sheet extents before 11, 500 years BP, are centered around different points than the present polar spin axes. Their differences are about 20 to 30 degrees of latitude at both poles. Why? A displaced crust and mantle easily address this question.

Secondly, why are the geomagnetic poles different by 15 to 25 degrees of latitude than the spin axes and drifting toward the north polar spin axis for the north geomagnetic pole? The south geomagnetic pole is drifting, but not directly toward the south pole.[25] The author is suggesting that the magnetic field generated by the spinning iron core causes a strong residual magnetism at the polar regions inside the mantle. If, and when, the mantle becomes displaced, the residual magnetism remains in the same location inside the mantle to establish a new geomagnetic pole location different from the one that was over the spin axis. Then, in subsequent thousands of years, the magnetic forces at the spin axis begin to develop a new residual magnetism and move the original residual magnetism, once again, toward the spin axis. Space probes have measured differences of spin axes and magnetic poles on other planets that suggests these planets, too, have liquid cores and mantle displacements caused by external electrical and magnetic disruptions. The Electric Universe community does not question that immense forces, due to electrical currents and magnetic forces between celestial bodies do occur. NASA, and the current accepted dogma, stubbornly refuses to accept that this transmission of EM forces occurs in space between celestial bodies, although Valles Marinaris of Mars looks at them directly in the face and tells them that only a very continuous and high energy electric arc sputtered material into space to create the largest, longest canyon in the solar system. No process of erosion could possibly have made this canyon that appears to be made by the path of a charged body passing overhead. Valles Marinaris on Mars was unquestionably caused by high energy arc discharge between two celestial bodies similar to the effect of a manufacturing process called electrical discharge machining (EDM).

### Figure 16. Wandering North Magnetic Pole Returning to Its Natural Home of the Earth's Spin Axis

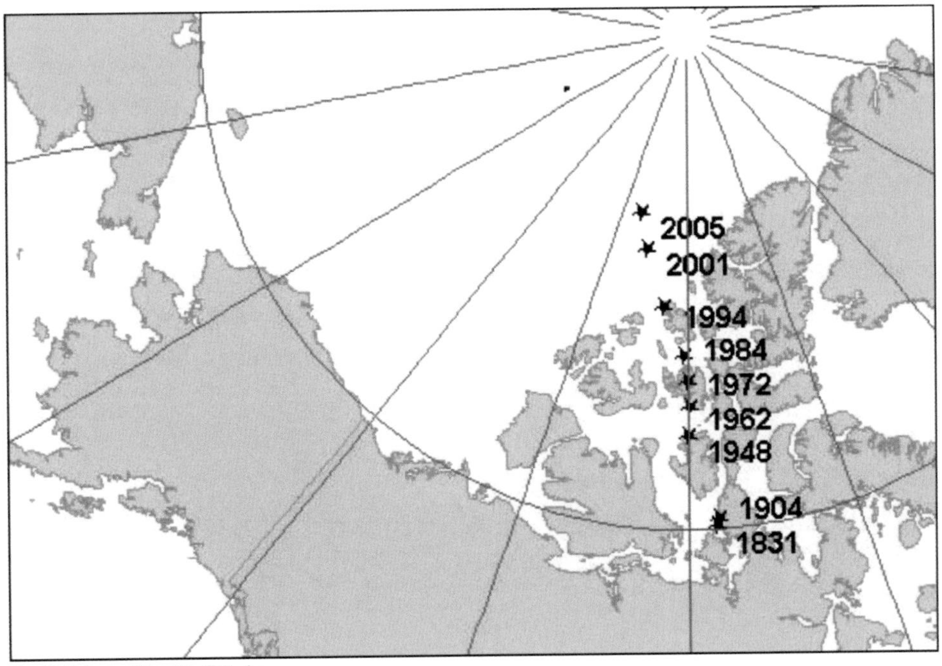

Credit: Science/HowStuffWorks

## Figure 17. Wandering South Magnetic Pole Seeking to Align with the Earth's Changing Dipole

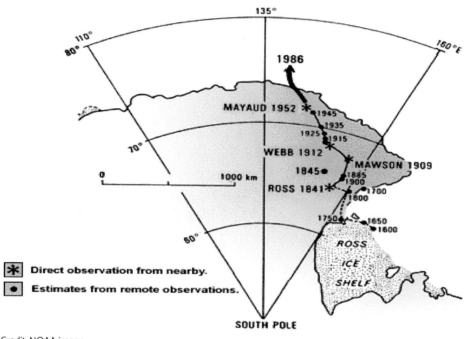

Credit: NOAA image

Thirdly, one should give careful attention to the topographical nature of the underwater ridges in the oceans, which represent the edges of tectonic plates. They are very well-defined by the newest, most modern mapping techniques. Many of the edges, especially in the Atlantic and Pacific plates, have repeated slip faults. Why? Because the plates' edges were pushed unevenly past each other after the displacing crust gained momentum unevenly in its motion of rotation southward along the meridian of 90 degrees west. The major magnetic and gravitational forces initially tugged at the existing north polar region along this 90-degree meridian supposedly defining the overhead path of the rogue planet. This line marked the closest approach producing the greatest electrical discharge and magnetic field affects. There is no other explanation for this massive slip faulting along most of the ridges' lengths, roughly parallel to this meridian line in both the Atlantic and Pacific Oceans. The tectonic plate theory can only explain why these rifts or oceanic ridges moved apart and not why they rubbed against each other causing slip faulting in a homogeneous fashion – unless, as is proposed, the entire crust and mantle was pulled briefly and inexorably southward, pole to pole, in the Western Hemisphere by external forces while still maintaining its original rotation from west to east in an equatorial direction.

This illustration shows the approximate location of the pre-diluvian north pole which was the geographical center of the Laurentide Ice Sheet.

The other pre-diluvian polar location was in the Southern Ocean off the coast of East Antarctic before it relocated to the center of the continent.

## C. YOUNGER DRYAS EVENT OCCURS OVER 1400 YEARS

An immediate question arises as to why such a catastrophic event and its aftermath would occur over such a long period of time as 1400 years. This period of time is marked clearly by the Younger Dryas geological period which is carefully dated and believed to have happened from 12,900 to 11,500 years ago BP.[16] Numerous proponents of the Great Deluge who connect the dots to the Younger Dryas believe it occurred at the end of the period due to evidence of massive deaths of flora and fauna that then became extinct during 11,500 years BP, with a margin of error of only about ± 100 years. The Younger Dryas is identified by a drastic cooling, occurring about 12,900 years ago BP, and then a dramatic warming period, occurring about 11,500 years BP (1400 years later), as measured in ice cores, particularly in the Greenland (GISP2) and the past Cariaco ice sheet region of Venezuela.

### 1. Arctic Ocean Freshwater Flux

What caused the sudden cooling that occurred 1400 years earlier, and is it connected somehow to the warming process? The most accepted theory is an Arctic freshwater forcing during the last deglaciation.[16] There was a decrease in the rate of North Atlantic Deep Water formation and a resulting weakening of the meridional, overturning circulation. According to computer simulations of a glacial systems model, the melting North American ice sheet contributed about half of the freshwater or meltwater pulse. At the beginning of the Younger Dryas, the largest freshwater influx was directed into the Arctic Ocean, blocking drainage, except for the Greenland-Iceland-Norwegian seas, where the North Atlantic Deep Water exchange is formed today. Hence, Lev Tarasov and W. R. Peltier of the Department of Physics of the University of Toronto hypothesized that the Arctic freshwater flux triggered the Younger Dryas cold reversal.[26]

### 2. Dust and $CO_2$-laden Atmosphere from Super-volcanoes

Another possible cause is the initiation of super-volcanoes over North America, such as the Yellowstone Caldera and the lesser known Long Valley Caldera, Valles Caldera and La Garita Caldera.[27] It is known that a single earthquake in any of these regions of the western United States can affect other earthquakes in the other caldera regions, including cone volcanoes in the states of the northwest and Alaska. This event is called an earthquake swarm which can possibly trigger simultaneously the eruption of several super-volcano calderas.[28] A dated explosion 13,800 years ago BP was determined for the Yellowstone Caldera, which is very close to the beginning of the Younger Dryas of

12,900 years BP. This explosion was due to a relatively smaller steam explosion that left a 3.1-mile diameter crater centered at Mary Bay on the edge of Yellowstone Lake. Other undetected eruptions could have been centered under Yellowstone Lake.[29] Regardless, the accurate determination of dating for eruptions that old is made difficult due to less opportunities for radiocarbon dating of organics and the partial melting of rock surrounding calderas with repeated explosions. The steam explosion information is from the "Introduction to hydrothermal (steam) explosions in Yellowstone" by Yellowstone National Park retrieved December 31, 2008.[30]

### 3. Large Error in Radiocarbon Dating for 12,900 Years Ago

Although the first two reasons are good possibilities, this paper favors that the timeline for the beginning of the Younger Dryas of 12,900 years BP is a serious error. Many uncertainties lead the author to believe that the measured dramatic cooling actually occurred much closer to, or even was initiated by, the Great Deluge event. The displacement of the Earth's geoid immediately moved the Laurentide ice sheet southward to a warmer latitude, causing a pulse of the freshwater influx. In addition, crust/mantle shift caused a new geoid, which in turn caused a multitude of earthquakes and volcanism and opening of the oceanic rifts. Due to the eruptions of vast amounts of subterranean dust, gases and water high into the atmosphere, accelerated cooling began to shield radiant heat energy from the Sun. The time period for recovery of the atmosphere and ice sheet adjustments is more like 200 to 500 years instead of the 1400 years currently thought to be the length of the Younger Dryas cool period. Hence, the beginning of the Younger Dryas is closer to 11,500 years BP and not 12,900 years BP. The duration of the Younger Dryas was more like 200 to 400 years lasting until 11,100 BP. Of course, many other effects, which are not precisely determined, lasted much longer.

The cooling and warming and freshwater influx actually happened as confirmed by the radiometry of oxygen/hydrogen isotopic methods, but radiocarbon dating was almost exclusively used for the dating process. In fact, the radiocarbon dating of the alpine-tundra Dryas octopetala plant that favors cooler climates gave the geological period its name.[31] Radiocarbon dating is a bona fide method that is excellent for time periods within 50,000 years, due to the half-life of the isotope carbon 14. However, this dating method relies on a fairly constant calibrated curve for achieving accurate results. Radiocarbon dating's basic assumption is that the ratio of isotopes $^{14}C/^{12}C$ can be represented by a calibration curve that remains the same over the preceding thousands of years. Isotope carbon 14 is supposedly produced at a constant rate in the atmosphere by the bombardment of cosmic rays.[32] The carbon-dating is confirmed by the matched dating of tree ring data and Egyptian chronology that has recently been extended from 8000 to 13,900 years. The tree ring data helps to design corrections to the calibration curve over time.[33] However, this author severely questions whether carbon dating can be utilized in the very volatile period during the Great Deluge event that occurred roughly from 11,500 to 11,000 years BP.

As previously mentioned, the Sun's celestial visitors increased the solar wind, added their own charged fields on close approach, and immensely increased the Earth's magnetic field. These effects will depress the amount of carbon-14 created in the atmosphere. And, these effects of atmospheric variations cannot and are not addressed or predicted currently in any carbon-dating calibration curve.[34] Furthermore, the $^{14}C/^{12}C$ age is further depressed immediately during and after the Great Deluge cataclysm due to:

a. Global conflagrations from the burning of organics, made possible by Earth's electrification that, in turn, increased lightning bolts from atmosphere to ground. This is similar to today's "fossil fuel effect" which is the contamination of ancient methane and $CO_2$ due to today's industrialization.[35]

b. The "hardwater effect" due to rivers passing over limestone and acquiring carbonate ions was caused by the accelerated melting of the ice sheets that were suddenly moved southward. This new freshwater influx makes the $^{14}C/^{12}C$ ratio appear thousands of years older for both the seawater and the organisms living in it. These new carbonate ions were never exposed to carbon-14 from the atmosphere.[36]

c. The "marine effect" comes into play because the mixing of deep and surface waters takes much longer than the mixing of atmospheric surface waters with C 14; hence, deep-water ocean volumes have an apparent age of several more thousands of years.[37] Normal correction for fractionation of about 940 years may not be enough during these chaotic times with accelerated ice sheet melting, especially that of the newly floating East Antarctic ice sheet, which greatly increases the deeper ocean mixing.

d. Volcanic eruptions, even those of super-volcanoes, and the hydroplates' much older waters, released from subterranean chambers under ocean ridges, have no detectable carbon-14, being underground for so long. Hence, the $^{14}C/^{12}C$ ratio is greatly depressed, which in turn depresses dating ages. It has been discovered that numerous buried plants near eruptions have depressed ages of about one thousand years.[38]

Clearly, the chaotic effects on Earth during the Great Deluge event can make it extremely difficult for researchers to use radiocarbon dating. But of course, these scientists are not expecting that such drastic changes to the radiocarbon calibration curve do occur. For more information, consult the sources by the following authors: Martin J. Aitken, Thomas S. Bianchi, Chabil Dass, Mark Maslin and Michael F. L'Annunziata concerning the science of radiocarbon dating.

The following figure from NOAA, National Oceanic and Atmospheric Administration, indicates with high definition the boundaries of the Younger Dryas period, using mostly radiocarbon dating.[39] However, the dating is seriously questioned because the assumed calibration curve is inappropriately utilized as was explained.

The following chart, Figure 19, shows a hypothetical radiocarbon calibration curve being used incorrectly during the Great Deluge episode because none of the previously mentioned effects of the $^{14}C/^{12}C$ ratio are applied. The indicated scaling is relative but shows how the age of flora, fauna, ice cores, sea sediments and volcanic rock can be dated incorrectly much earlier than what is actually the true case. A depressed ratio where $^{14}C$ is reduced and $^{12}C$ is greatly increased is due to the chaotic conditions that occurred throughout the Great Deluge event.

The depressed radiocarbon calibration curve also indicates that both the first and second freshwater fluxes were shifted incorrectly and spread over a longer span of time than would be expected. Indeed, the first freshwater flux was caused by the very shortened melting of the northern ice sheets, especially the Laurentide in North America. A space of time between the first and second flux was due to the almost complete depletion of the Laurentide Ice Sheet. This ice sheet was completely destroyed and melted by the tremendously hot and explosive electrical discharges that struck Earth coming from the passing rogue celestial body. These thunderbolts of current entered Earth in the Hudson Bay region where the ancient magnetic dipole existed. The second freshwater flux was eventually caused by the slower melting of the floating East Antarctica Ice Sheet (EAIS) due to a colder Earth that was shielded by a very dusty atmosphere. After the dust settled and the Earth became warmer, thermohaline circulation between less salty southern oceans and the northern oceans began. Mixing of the fresher southern oceans with more salts in the northern oceans created the second measured freshwater flux, which spanned much less time than what is given by the standard calibration curve.

A very important feature of the depressed curved is that, in all likelihood, it flattened while the $^{14}C/^{12}C$ ratio started to recover. This flattened curve produced a large majority of natural history specimens that peaked around the time of 11,500 years BP, indicating a definitive boundary for the end of the Younger Dryas period and flagging a dramatic change in climate.

Both freshwater fluxes actually started much closer to the deluge event of 11,500 years BP as would be expected. The unknown depressed radiocarbon calibration curve greatly exaggerated their time spans and starting times. The start time for the first flux actually should move to the right on the curve, and the start time for the second flux should move to the left. The time span between the two fluxes should be very brief in 10's of years.

## Figure 18. Younger Dryas Climate Anomalies

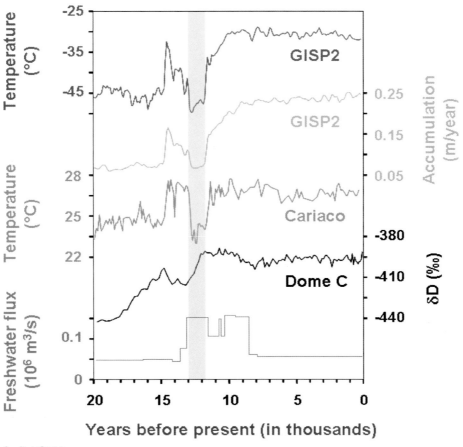

Credit: NOAA Image

The above chart shows Younger Dryas climate anomalies in Greenland, the Cariaco Basin in Venezuela, Antarctica and freshwater forcing or flux of meltwater from the Laurentide Ice Sheet down the St. Lawrence River. The chart is presented by NOAA, National Oceanic and Atmospheric Administration's Paleoclimatology Branch and the National Climatic Data Center.[41]

## Figure 19. Results of Anomalous Depressed Radiocarbon Calibration Curve

Inappropriate Use of Radiocarbon Dating During the Younger
Dryas Geological Period When the Great Deluge Event Occurred

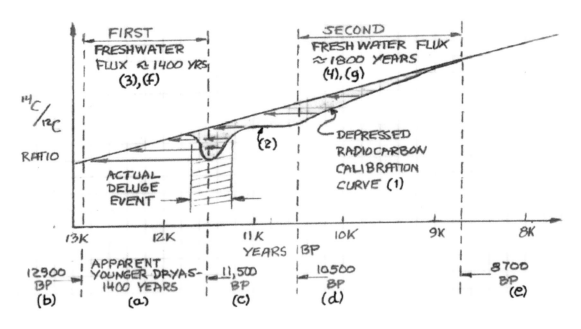

## NOTES ON FIGURE 19

[1]   Anomalous depressed radiocarbon calibration curve that makes specimens seen older.

[2]   The curve likely flattens to indicate the maximum number of Younger Dryas specimens being dated at 11,500 years BP.

[3]   First freshwater flux spanning 1400 years.

[4]   Second freshwater flux spanning 1800 years.

[a]   Predicted Younger Dryas is 1400 years long, but actually took place in a much shorter time span as is indicated by the calibration curve.

[b]   Radical cooling and increase in freshwater flux at 12,900 years BP that actually occurred closer to 11,500 years BP.

[c]   Radical warming and decrease in freshwater flux at 11,500 years BP that actually occurred 200 or more years later over a longer span of time.

[d]   Beginning of second cycle of freshwater flux dated at 10,500 years BP.

[e]   Decrease and end of second flux cycle dated at 8,700 years BP.

[f]   Span of time taken to melt most of the northern hemisphere's ice sheets due to high energy discharges and Laurentide Ice Sheet moving southward.

[g]   Span of time taken to melt most of the Eastern Antarctica Ice Sheet that calved and/or slid into the ocean.

## D. ANTARCTICA'S DOME C ICE CORE DATING, ACCORDING TO RESEARCHERS, IS 800,000 YEARS OLD

Obviously, a serious discrepancy occurs with the dating of the oldest ice core in East Antarctica at location Dome C. If major pieces of the East Antarctica ice sheet slid into the ocean about 11,500 years BP, then how can a deep ice core in this ice sheet be 800,000 years old? This revelation becomes a significant challenge to the hypothesis being promoted by this paper.

The confidence in the chronology is lessened the lower in the ice sheet one goes, due to high pressures and squeezing that causes horizontal movements. The annual oscillations slowly decrease, relative to other factors, such as atmospheric dust variance due to volcanic eruptions. These markers are fewer and farther apart because they are not recorded by other means. The identification of layers will probably limit the number of countable annual layers to less than about 8,500 years, which is younger than the age of the Great Deluge event (Hammer, et al., 1978).[40] This compression and smearing of the individual layers is compounded by an assertion that the pre-deluge East Antarctica Ice Sheet (EAIS) was thicker by 1.2 to 1.5 times its present thickness. So, credible and accurate dating to within hundreds or thousands of years for ice cores any older than 8500 years is almost impossible.

However, the technique used to estimate the age of deeper ice layers is to measure the differential isotope content of $^{18}O$ and compute the atmospheric temperature which is observed to produce such concentrations today (Jouzel and Merlivat, 1984).[41] This method is considered indisputable when a second-known relation between temperature and precipitation rate, again observed in today's atmosphere, is correlated with the previous data. The accumulation rate is then calculated for given layer groupings (Lorius, et al., 1985).[42] Once the accumulation rate is calculated for each "virtual" layer, the depth and age for each apparent layer in the ice is then calculated by integrating the annual accumulation downward from the surface. The process uses the questionable assumptions that correlations stay constant through the millennia and that the mathematics of integration is verification. No direct reading of radiometric or other isotopic data is ever taken. However, these findings correlate very well with other information of glaciation periods, including their glacials and interglacials. Therefore, a reasonable confidence of the technique is achieved. See the chart for showing composite data for Dome C's $CO_2$ (ppm) going back nearly 800,000 years, and related glacial cycles (Wikipedia, Ice Core, 2016).[43]

The only possibility of having 800,000-year-old ice is that not all the ice sheet of East Antarctica slid or calved into the ocean during the Great Deluge. The ice cores of Dome C, Vostok, and Dome A are well-inland and sitting on some of thickest parts of the ice sheet. More importantly, these research stations sit on the ice divides where the measured ice velocity goes either toward West Antarctica or toward the ocean (AntarcticaGlaciers.org).[44] The East Antarctic Ice Sheet has received less scientific attention than West Antarctica. Its extent at the Last Glacial Maximum is poorly resolved and its interior's geomorphology is less well understood. Hence, only a certain large portion of this older ice, dated at 160,000 to 800,000 years, slid into the ocean, but certainly enough to cause sudden global flooding. The ice sheet was separated inland near the ice divide and only the ice sheet portions on the ocean side of the continental ice divide slid into the ocean. Deep ice cores closer to the ocean need to be generated to prove this point. But, research stations are difficult to establish in these areas because it is high, cold, windy and inaccessible. The present Antarctic Ice-Core Stations and their locations, with elevations, are shown in the following map.

Figure 20. Maps of Antarctica showing locations and elevations in meters above sea level (masl) of Law Dome (1390 masl); Dome C (3233 masl); Taylor Dome (2365 masl); Vostok (3500 masl); Dome A (4084 masl), the South Pole station (2810 masl); and Siple Station (1054 masl).

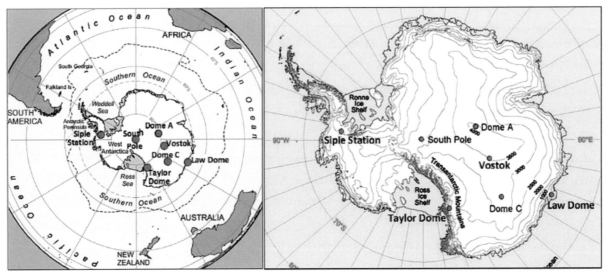

Credit: Antarctic Ice-Core Station Maps Image

Another radical but serious viewpoint about the ice core data is expressed by a creationist scientist. The following direct quote is taken from "Ice Cores and the Age of the Earth" by Larry Vardiman, Ph.D., which supports that the ice core data is misunderstood because the effects of the Great Flood are not taken into account.

"There are several historical markers in Antarctica which can be used to cross check these calculations for the past few thousand years. But historical volcanic events are not known beyond a few thousand years in the past which provide any certainty to the calculation of age. This method would be reasonably reliable if precipitation rates had been similar in the past. However, some creationist models predict significant quantities of snow immediately after the Flood (Oard, 1990).[45] Perhaps as much as 95% of the ice near the poles could have accumulated in the first 500 years or so after the Flood.

"It would be extremely valuable to thoroughly explore these ice-core data. We would not assume that the precipitation rate has always been similar to that of today. We would expect considerably higher precipitation rates immediately following the Flood. The layers of ice near the bottom of the core should be thicker than expected by the uniformitarian model and contain unusual excursions in $\delta^{18}O$, acidity, and particulates from levels higher in the core. The "annual" layers deep in the Greenland ice sheet may be related to individual storms rather than seasonal accumulations. If these evidences are found, direct information on conditions following the Flood would be available to us.

"Nothing in the ice-core data from either Greenland or Antarctica requires the Earth to be of great age. In fact, there are good reasons to believe that the ice cores are revealing important information about conditions following the Flood of Genesis and the recent formation of thick ice sheets. Reports of ice-core data containing records of climatic changes as far back as 160,000 years in the past are dependent upon interpretations of these data which could be seriously wrong, if the Genesis Flood occurred as described in the Bible. Further research on ice-core data should be a high priority for creationist researchers."

Figure 21. Antarctica Ice Core Data Based on Atmospheric
CO₂ Showing Glacial Cycles for Past 800,000 Years

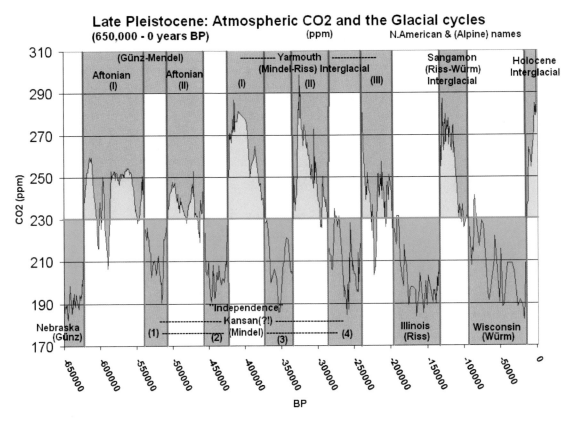

Credit: Wikipedia Ice Core Image

Figure 22. Antarctica Ice Core Data of Ice Age Temperature Changes
and Ice Volume (Evidence of Postulated Large Increases After
12,000 Years Ago Are Shown and Expected for Reestablishing the EAIS)

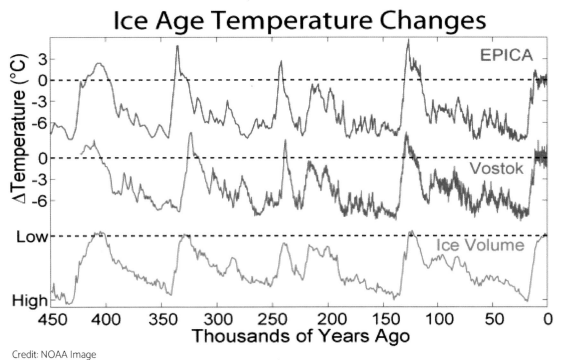

Credit: NOAA Image

# VIII.

# CONDITIONS CAUSING EAST ANTARCTICA'S ICE SHEET TO SLIDE INTO THE SEA

The process of having large portions of EAIS float into the ocean is rather complicated. The previous diagram of Figure 14 illustrates the likely steps that occurred from pre-deluge to present times.

1. The ice sheet is 1.5 to 1.2 times thicker during pre-deluge times than today, causing a phase change at a certain depth that becomes pressurized water; a slushy layer and/or subglacial lakes are then created. These subglacial lakes occur even today in the deepest parts of the ice sheet. The pressure-temperature phase diagram of water shows a negative slope of the line between the solid and liquid phases that indicates the freezing point decreases with increasing pressure, for a certain amount of pressure range, before turning into ice once again (Wikipedia.org/wiki/Subglacial lake).[46] During the pre-deluge times, this slushy and watery boundary occurred well above bedrock and also above older ice that already formed. The ice sheet components were still very stable, due to variations in pressure that created contact points through this slippery boundary. Also, at this time, sea level was lower than the isostatic compressed bed rock.

2. During the subject catastrophic event the entire crust and mantle of Earth was shifted southward roughly along the 75° West meridian line and northward along the 105° East meridian line. Antarctica was displaced about 25 to 30 degrees of latitude, causing the south pole axis to then be located in the center of the continent, as opposed to the original location off the coast of East Antarctica near Law Dome. The Earth's geoid then sank farther into the mantle, due to less centripetal force being applied to the mantle and crust at this location. The potential sinking for a 30-degree displacement of latitude is approximately 1/3 x 6 miles on Earth's radius or 2 miles. This region, being closer to the pole, probably resulted in much less change – perhaps less than ¼ to ½ mile or more than 1000 feet. In addition, the southern displacement of the northern ice sheets accelerated their melting and calving into the Arctic Ocean, thereby quickly raising sea level.

This combination of sea level rising and bedrock sinking, due to geoid adjustments, brought EAIS's slushy boundary well under sea level, thereby floating and separating the ice sheet above this boundary. The motion dynamics of the entire bedrock shifting horizontally then caused large portions of the ice sheet to move horizontally in the opposite direction toward and into the ocean. Large pieces of ice sheet were no longer sitting on land but floating in the ocean. Hence, sea level began to rise continuously, similar to dropping ice cubes into a glass of water to raise its water level. Some of the older ice below the slushy boundary in various locations remained on the bedrock and did not slide into the ocean. For this reason, ice older than 11,500 years had its much older age documented by ice core analyses.

3. After most of the weight of the ice sheets of East Antarctica was removed from the bedrock, isostatic adjustments made the elevation rise slowly. Eventually, sea level, also slowly, would be lowered as the climates, winds and ocean currents made adjustments. Water inventories would once again transfer from the oceans to new ice sheets on both West and East Antarctica. Greenland's ice sheet had serious melting, but retained some of its extent and then regained more ice. The Arctic Ocean would also freeze and collect a build-up of snow and ice.

The current conditions are that the EAIS is sitting mostly on bedrock above sea level, creating fairly stable conditions. However, West Antarctica's Ice Sheet currently rests on ground about 52 feet below sea level, which makes it potentially unstable (Ivins, E.R. 2009).[47] West Antarctica gained much more ice after subsequent climatic adjustments produced thick ice sheets, causing the bedrock to sink. Prior to the Great Deluge event, West Antarctica was sitting 30 degrees of latitude farther from the South Pole, above sea level because warmer conditions caused less ice build-up.

Some examples of glacial landforms come from James Ross Island, which is located on the northeast tip of the Antarctic Peninsula, at about 64°S in West Antarctica. The area was glaciated during the Last Glacial Maximum, with cosmogenic nuclide exposure ages indicating a recession of the main glacier ice around 11,000 to 9500 years ago which abides by this paper's hypothesis. The landscape is now characterized by permafrost, with small cold and polythermal glaciers and periglacial landforms.[48] What really happened prior to 11,000 ago is that very little ice existed, due to James Ross Island being about 30-degrees latitude farther north from the South Pole during an interglacial period. Then the landmass suddenly shifted much closer to the South Pole, forming new glaciers on West Antarctica and peri-glaciation on James Ross Island.

Refer to the "Marine Ice Sheet Instability Hypothesis" for more information about another possible global deluge coming from the instability of the Western Antarctic Ice Sheet (WAIS).[49]

# IX.
# MORE EVIDENCE FOR THE
# SOUTH POLAR REGION'S HISTORY

Just as is indicated at the North Pole, the center of the coldest portions of land mass prior to 11,500 years ago is located about 25 to 30 degrees of latitude away from the present South Pole axis. Glaciers at that time were shown as being largest in East Antarctica and to lesser extent in Tasmania and southern New Zealand.[50] No heavy glaciation was present in West Antarctica and southern South America, which today are closer to the pole than land masses on the opposite side of East Antarctica. This kind of evidence leads to the obvious reasoning of a crustal/mantle shift that corresponds with the north polar region.

The South Magnetic pole is offset in a similar fashion as the North Magnetic pole, and both are still wandering. The offset is interpreted as being the location of the crust/mantle before the Great Deluge's resulting mantle shift. The mantle's memory of its original magnetic field is continually being affected and adjusted by the Earth's inner core dynamo, which attempts to align its magnetic field's dipole with the spinning axis. The offsets roughly follow the 75° meridian line that closely goes through Venezuela. The radiocarbon dating of glaciers for temperatures and deaths of extinct animals in Venezuela's mountainous region of Cariaco perfectly match those found in the northern polar regions.[18] This mountainous region was moved from a temperate zone to an equatorial zone 30° southward where sudden melting would take place. The interpretation is that high energy plasma passed along a swath of Earth's surface between the meridian lines of 65° and 85°, traveling from the North to South polar regions, both electrifying and magnetizing the crust along its path, killing flora and fauna and contributed to melting mountainous ice sheets.

The freshwater flux measurements that help define the Younger Dryas indicate that the flux started dramatically about 12,900 years BP and then slowed for a period of 800 years, before increasing to previous high levels, and then finally ending about 9000 years BP. The level of freshwater flux and its periodicity are not seriously questioned, but the absolute dating in years is in doubt due to reasons already explained by the radiocarbon calibration system's being inappropriately utilized for these chaotic times. However, the interpretation is very clear. The first period of freshwater flux was due to the primary and quick melting of the north polar region's ice sheets. The second fairly sustained period of freshwater flux is due to very large chunks of ice, probably the size of the state of Connecticut, coming from the East Antarctica Ice Sheet and melting slowly in the southern seas. The melting and evaporation processes would eventually transfer the ice volume from the sea back to the East Antarctica land mass.

Another large collection of data is presented as further evidence. *The first 10,000 years of ice taken from East Antarctica ice cores is an excellent reflection of new ice sheet build-up since the Great Deluge when major parts of the ice sheet slid into the ocean.* This data is the "$N_2O$, $CH_4$, and $CO_2$ Data from Dome C Ice Core (Antarctica) Covering the Holocene, NOAA/NCDC/WDC Paleoclimatology".[51] The following charts of Figure 23 for these atmospheric compounds illustrates how their concentrations change from 11,000 years ago to present times, when rapid climatic changes took place. As is expected, these gases, $CO2$, $CH_4$, and $N_2O$, would peak after the Great Deluge event when massive volcanism occurred and oceanic ridges erupted. As the crust slowly healed itself and eruptions slowed, these measured gases soon decreased, as the subject charts reveal. The ice cores for this data were drilled to a maximum of 1200 feet. Beyond this depth, the layers are very obscured and could not be used to collect annualized data; the reason is rather obvious. The blue ice beneath this depth goes back to a much earlier age when there was an ice sheet much thicker on top than now. Today, this ice above an older non-existent slushy layer is also non-existent, since it slid into the ocean. New, annualized layers of ice have replaced the older ice since the Great Deluge. The graphs in Figure 23 are found by searching Google Images for "$N_2O$, $CH_4$, and $CO_2$ Data from Dome C Ice Core (Antarctica) Covering the Holocene, NOAA/NCDC/WDC Paleoclimatology".

These following charts also indicate that the data collected at Dome C corroborates good alignment between $CO_2$, $CH_4$, $N_2O$ for the first 10,000 years which is expected. The other glacial periods or special geological events that go back further from 600,000 to 800,000 years BP are not used for any evidence for this paper. Dome C ice cores are taken well inland where much deeper ice that did not slide into the ocean was encountered. However, due to the blurring of annualized data that goes back further than 8500 years, this data is suspicious. Data much older than 10,000 years can only be obtained through mathematical integration and extrapolation.

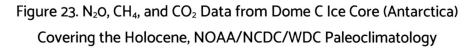

Figure 23. $N_2O$, $CH_4$, and $CO_2$ Data from Dome C Ice Core (Antarctica)
Covering the Holocene, NOAA/NCDC/WDC Paleoclimatology

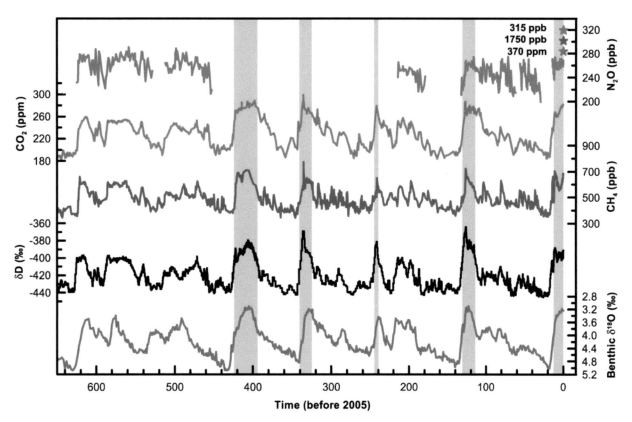

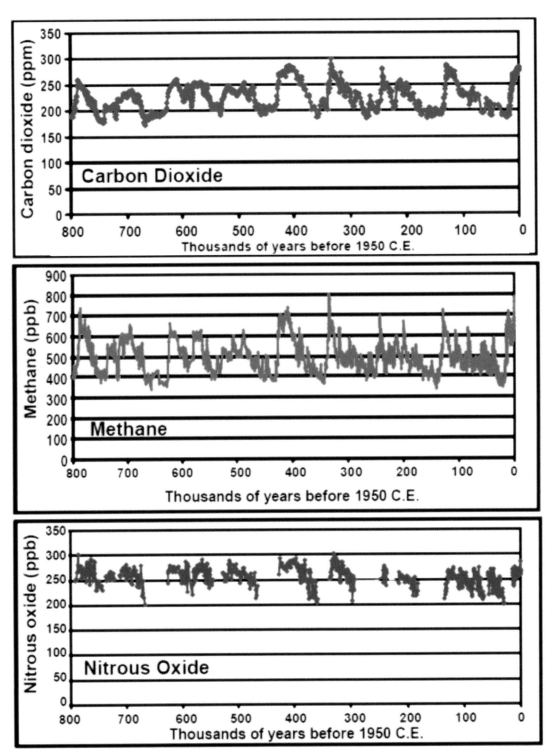

Atmospheric carbon dioxide ($CO_2$), methane ($CH_4$), and nitrous oxide ($N_2O$) derived from air bubbles trapped in ice at Dome C, Antarctica. Units are parts per million (ppm) for $CO_2$ and parts per billion (ppb) for $CH_4$ and $N_2O$. Year zero can be taken as 1950 of the Christian Era (C.E.) Minus signs indicate years before 1950 C.E.

Credit: NOAA Image

# X.
# THE HYDROPLATE HYPOTHESIS

A quick snapshot of the *hydroplate hypothesis,* or theory, as it is referred to by its originator, Dr. Walt Brown,[52] follows. Large amounts of water, almost half of Earth's estimated volume (a much lesser amount is proposed by this paper), was stored at an estimated 10-mile depth in subterranean chambers that were mostly interconnected prior to the Great Deluge. The water was under very high pressure in the supercritical phase, and through tidal pumping had enough movement to dissolve minerals and salts that collected on the chambers' floors. The roof and columns containing this supercritical water (SCW) were called *hydroplates* by Brown; hence the *hydroplate theory* was born.

The tidal pumping continued to heat and pressurize the SCW until the Earth's crust stretched to the breaking point along the oceanic ridges, opening them almost simultaneously like a zipper. These globe-circling ruptures released the SCW which exploded violently from its hydroplate chambers and then it was jettisoned supersonically upward, through the atmosphere and far above, where it expanded and cooled before falling as dirty rain, hail and muck, which contained large quantities of dissolved minerals such as limestone, salt and silicates. This precipitation, in combination with freezing and violent winds, caused the Holocene extinction event.

The aftermath starts with the collapse of the hydroplates, causing continental shelves and slopes and the quick rise in sea level. Larger chunks of expelled materials created comets/asteroids that were launched into space, supposedly reaching escape velocities. During the flood stage, most fossils and limestone formed, including sediments and fossils sorted and layered by liquefaction. The mid-ocean ridges formed, causing rapid continental drift, principally away from the Atlantic oceanic ridge. Crustal compression events caused major mountain ranges, metamorphic rock formation, the enigmatic rocky over-thrusts to form and geothermal heating due to internal friction between the mantle and outer liquid core. The rise of mountain ranges and continental drift caused an unbalanced condition that started the Earth to roll and become tilted, explaining the changing paths of the stars and Sun across the sky.

Brown's resulting aftermath of the ruptured hydroplates opposes, belittles and severely attacks the accepted scientific dogma and paradigms. His style of science is trying very passionately to match Biblical accounts, as though they can be completely trusted and interpreted properly. Many enigmatic geological phenomena, such as metamorphic rock forming, knowing that water cannot seep deeper than about 5 miles; uniform differentiated sedimentary rock; mountainous sedimentary rock folded like it was the consistency of putty; rapid burial of unexplainably large amounts of limestone; sunken plateaus with horizontal rock layers with surrounding vertically squeezed mountains; and numerous others he answers very well with excellent arguments.

I remain open-minded about many of his explanations, except flatly rejecting those for:

1. the hydroplates creation of asteroids and comets

2. the *amount* of water held in the hydroplate reservoirs and its total volume released during the Great Deluge

3. the formation of all sedimentary and metamorphic rock produced in only one event

4. the rapid spread of continents, within days, away from the Atlantic oceanic ridge after it was opened

5. the Earth's axis slowly rolling about 30 degrees due to an imbalance from continental shift.

## A. WALT BROWN'S BOOK, *IN THE BEGINNING*

Walt Brown, Ph.D., published his 8th edition of the book, *In the Beginning: Compelling Evidence for the Creation and the Flood*, in 2008 and has a website at creationscience.com. Brown is labeled as a creationist who is both a scientist and supporter of the Bible. He makes an excellent scientific case for why the theory of organic evolution does not work; however, this paper will concentrate on Brown's hydroplate hypothesis and his ideas about the frozen mammoths. His ideas probably originated with the Christian biblical story of the Great Deluge that includes how the rain from the Deep bowels of the Earth lasted for 40 days and nights. I certainly do not support a verbatim belief in a God-given book, but like Brown, I believe the storyline of Genesis and the Great Deluge have a scientific basis and are essential for understanding Earth's and mankind's history. These embellished, but real, stories were handed down, at first verbally, and then by written word from the earliest of times by the few survivors.

Brown's overview of his hydroplate theory is illustrated. I do not accept that the hydroplate roof is granitic. The entire ocean floor, including any magna overflow from a rift, is entirely basaltic rock. Also, this author does not endorse Brown's fast phase of continental drift, caused by the release of extreme amounts of upward energy that force the plates horizontally in opposite directions away from the rift of the ridge's origin.

Brown's chapter on "The Hydroplate Theory: An Overview" is an amazing read which is required to understand his hypothesis which is in direct opposition to plate tectonics. Brown believes he meets the criteria for evaluating theories which are listed:

1. The <u>process</u> must explain all relevant observations better than any other proposed explanation so as to increase its confidence level.

2. The theory must be <u>parsimonious</u> in using the fewest assumptions; using few assumptions allows the theorist to explain many things and confidence is greater.

3. Published <u>predictions</u> are the most important test of any scientific theory.

This author is impressed with his hypothesis and believes Brown has met these criteria. Brown and the author have basic differences, but overall these ideas support the Great Deluge event described in this paper. This paper only attempts to cover the Earth's history for the past 22,000 years that includes accepted methods for dating and recognizing fossil records of the Pleistocene transition and Holocene eras. To my amazement, Brown attempts to explain the complete fossil record of Earth, continental drift, the rise of most mountain ranges, limestone and methane origin and most of the formation of sedimentary and metamorphic rock by using his hydroplate theory and the one Great Deluge event described in the Christian Bible. This paper accepts his hydroplate theory, but not the encompassing formation of all of Earth's organic fossils and transitional rocks. The author of this paper supports that numerous and similar events, like the Great Deluge, could have occurred at other times within the last hundreds of millions of years and that the hydroplate process, among others, was involved. The extinction events of the dinosaurs and mammoths, and of other eras, unlike Brown's determination, are separated by perhaps millions of years. Brown is very controversial in postulating that after the mid-Atlantic ridge forms, rapid continental drift begins, most fossils and limestone form, coal/oil/salt domes form, sediments and fossils are sorted and layered by liquefaction and numerous other geological/geophysical events all occurred since the Great Flood of 11,500 years ago when the hydroplates ruptured.

## Figure 24. Overview of 'Hydroplate' Theory

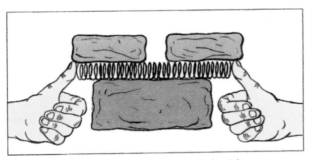

a) Overlying rocks keep a compressed spring horizontal.

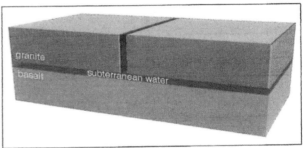

d) Rupture completed. Jetting water not shown.

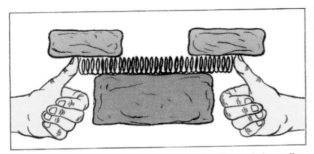

b) The spring remains aligned and compressed as the gap between the rocks widens.

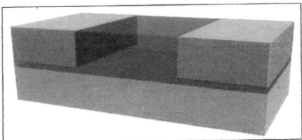

e) The rupture's path widens by the crushing, erosion, and collapse of the vertical walls, exposing part of the chamber floor. Most of earth's sediments are quickly produced by escaping, high-velocity waters—the fountains of the great deep.

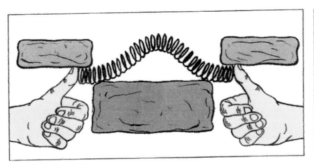

c) When the gap reaches a certain critical width, the spring *suddenly* buckles upward. Now consider thousands of similar springs lined up behind the first spring—all linked together and repeating in unison steps a–c. The upward buckling of any spring will cause adjacent springs to become unstable and buckle up themselves. They, in turn, will lift the next spring, and so on, in ripple fashion.

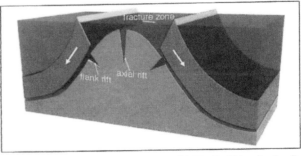

f) Continental-drift phase begins. The Mid-Atlantic Ridge "springs" upward, releasing extreme amounts of energy inherent in compressed rock. Fracture zones form perpendicular to the ridge axis; rifts form along the ridge axis. [See Endnote 57 on page 136.] The massive hydroplates, lubricated by water, begin to accelerate downhill. As more and more weight slides away from the newly-formed ridge, the exposed chamber floor quickly rises several miles (accelerating the hydroplates even more) and becomes the Atlantic floor. (In the next chapter, you will see other phenomenon and events that made the downhill slope very steep.)

· Spring Analogy Showing Development of the Mid-Atlantic Ridge.

Credit: Walt Brown's Image

## 1. Different Ideas and Opinions

Obviously, Walt Brown and the author of this paper have grave differences in our individual hypotheses. However, let's not be hasty in throwing away this unique and valuable hydroplate theory. The theory has much merit and is utilized, in part, to explain the Great Deluge event of this paper. Brown's key assumption is that "about half the water now in the oceans was once in interconnected chambers about 10 miles below most of the Earth's surface. At thousands of locations the chamber's sagging ceiling pressed against the chamber's floor. These extensive, solid contacts are called pillars. The average thickness of the subterranean water was about ¾ mile. Above the subterranean water was a granite crust; beneath the water was a layer of basaltic rock. All this ancient, stored, pressurized water was released over a very short period of hours or days with the subsequent collapse of the chamber's ceiling on a global scale.

This author will now challenge Brown's starting assumption to produce something more realistic.

a.  In a previous chapter of this paper, credit is given to water under the ruptured hydroplates being a volume equivalent to 20 feet of sea level change and causing an unprecedented amount of precipitation. Hence, the stated "half the water now in the oceans" and "¾ mile of thickness" do not apply for this paper. Much of Earth's water inventory was already sitting on top, both in the form of ice and normal liquid. Much water may have been released in previously older hydroplate releases.

b.  Assuming that the *entire* Earth had this hydroplate layer is not pertinent. Lighter volatiles, like water and $CO_2$, percolating upward through the viscous mantle can form clusters of interconnected pressurized chambers of hot water under the hardened crust, but certainly not evenly distributed throughout and under all of Earth's crust. Geological hot spots, such as Hawaii and the Pacific's Ring of Fire, do not support Brown's idea even though volcanoes do release great amounts of water and $CO_2$. The contention by this paper is that hydroplates occur sporadically and in specific regions, such as near the oceanic ridges.

c.  Currently, the continents have mostly a lighter granitic rock and the heavier oceanic crusts are basaltic, which counters Brown's assumption that the granitic crust or hydroplate is above the chambers, and the floor is basaltic rock. Also, no explanation is given as to why the past and current separation of granitic and basaltic rocks occurred.

d. Brown's perfect world accepts that all hydroplates ruptured and released all the stored ancient water at one time and now such future hydroplate events can be forgotten. It is hoped this is the case, but more hydroplates may be waiting to be ruptured; perhaps all the subterranean water has been released over several separated eras of time causing other, older mass extinction events.

## 2. Hydroplates Support the Earth's Metamorphosis Hypothesis

The hydroplate theory, with the above listed limitations, is much favored for this paper because it neatly dovetails with the author's "The Earth's Metamorphosis (EMM) Hypothesis" found in the website, ettingerjournals.com. The EMM hypothesis explains the genesis of the Earth/Moon system that begins with Earth's being struck and penetrated by an icy orb 4 billion years ago. This orb, similar in composition and size to Jupiter's moon, Ganymede, brought lighter volatiles such as water, methane, ammonia and $CO_2$ to Earth's heavier, rocky mantle that had already been differentiated with lighter volatiles coming to the surface. The extra volume also enlarged the Earth's diameter, thereby cracking the existing crust. This hardened crust partially trapped the escaping volatiles and still does to this present time. Through differentiation and centrifuge processes, the volatiles continued to be separated and trapped, and escaped through cracks and fissures termed rifts and volcanoes. These new volatiles added to the forming oceans and atmosphere. Naturally, Walt Brown's hydroplate hypothesis is a welcome idea for supporting both the Great Deluge event and the Earth's metamorphosis hypothesis, but is being constrained and regulated for the above-listed reasons.

"The Earth's Metamorphosis Hypothesis" explains why the basaltic rocks are found on the ocean bottom and why mostly granitic materials are found on the continents. The basaltic rock was the original cooled crust and the lighter granitic rock is formed from the flow of a mixture of icy orb materials and the Earth's mantle erupting from the giant impact crater that began the first mega-continent. This penetrating impact can then explain why the Earth's mantle had a second differentiation of volatiles to form the hydroplate reservoirs of water. Walt Brown does not provide an explanation as to why his hydroplates formed or why the continental crusts are mostly granitic. But, Brown does superbly provide the reasons for the erupting hydroplates creating a lethal continuous fall of rain, hail and muck from the sky. However, his thinking about what triggered the eruption and about comets being created by the jettisoned water are inappropriate. Perhaps the jetting of high energy fountains, as Brown postulates, did create much of the unexplained large stone erratics and other aerial falls of various materials that are scattered around the world.

### 3. The Subterranean Supercritical Water (SCW)

Brown expertly postulates that the subterranean water is supercritical and cannot boil. He estimates a depth of 10 miles for subterranean chambers, which imposes a pressure of 62,000 psi that highly compresses the chamber walls to seal them. A tidal pumping lifts and settles the chamber ceiling twice a day due to Moon tides causing continuous heating to exceed the critical temperature of 705 °F. As the temperature continued to increase, the pressure in turn increased, to stretch the chambers and crust. Some minerals then dissolved in this supercritical water (SCW), especially limestone ($CaCO_3$), salt (NaCl) and quartz ($SiO_2$). SCW can dissolve salt up to about 840 °F. At higher temperatures, all salt precipitates out, which explains salt domes and the huge amounts of salt dispersed on the surface.

As the rupture and jetting of the SCW began, triggered by the Earth's crustal/mantle shift, the pressure dropped to almost zero in seconds, giving all fluid downstream tremendous kinetic energy. This huge acceleration expanded the spacing between water molecules, allowing flash evaporation, sudden cooling and even greater expansion, acceleration and cooling. Therefore, most of the vast thermal, electrical, chemical and surface energy in the subterranean water ended up not as heat at the Earth's surface, but as extreme kinetic energy in all fountains of the great Deep.

The mixture of SCW and $CO_2$ have great dissolving power with tidal pumping, and will break up and dissolve more of the solids than relatively stagnant liquid. Liquid droplets quickly formed and evaporated dissolved solids that precipitated as sediments on the floor. As the flood and jetting began, the escaping subterranean water swept most of these loose sediments on the chamber floors upward very high into the atmosphere. As the pressure in the supercritical fluid suddenly dropped, the liquid evaporated explosively and created precipitates of snow-like solid. Three common precipitates as previously mentioned, limestone ($CaCO_3$), salt (NaCl) and quartz ($SiO_2$), rained down with hail and rain from the sky on the surprised and unsuspecting inhabitants of Earth. These falling solids formed the loess soils over vast regions containing an unusual amount of limestone and salt minerals.

## B. SUDDEN DEATH OF MEGAFAUNA

The hydroplate theory needs a few more ingredients to set the stage for the better known, very sudden, death and quick freezing of megafauna in the north polar regions of Alaska and Siberia. The crustal/mantle shift of about 20 to 30 degrees along a meridian line brought these areas closer to the new North Pole, especially Siberia. As mentioned previously, a very charged and magnetic celestial body came close enough to shift the already highly-magnetized crust and mantle of Earth. These very strong EM forces are postulated to be initiated in the north polar region and abruptly pull the mantle southward roughly along the 75° West meridian line. These forces ripped apart the crust at the Arctic Ocean's oceanic ridge that is a continuation of the Atlantic Ocean rift that runs through Iceland, through the Greenland Basin, across the Arctic Ocean basin and then through western Siberia. This sudden opening of the Arctic Ocean rift released the supercritical, highly pressurized water trapped under that area's hydroplates. Hence, the instant dry freeze, sudden burials and suffocation of megafauna, as well as many smaller animals, in nearby Alaska and Siberia 11,500 years ago are explained. The combination of the explosive evaporation of the SCW that was shot high into the atmosphere, along with ejection of cold Arctic waters, and the almost instant movement of the Siberian crust toward the new North Pole, caused the super-freezing conditions, compared to the modern process of freeze-drying frozen foods. Of course, the solid materials brought by the jetting of the hydroplates laid down thick layers of loess that both suffocated and buried these large animals suddenly, even while still standing.

## 1. Geographical Extent

It is suggested that other, but not all, hydroplates in different areas of the globe released SCW, but their ejecta was not as efficient in performing a large kill-off as what happened in the north polar regions, especially Siberia. The other oceanic ridges are farther away from land masses, and the water already covering the existing oceanic ridges would greatly buffer the forces of the subterranean jetting. The Arctic Ocean has the shallowest average depth of 3400 ft. whereas the Pacific and Atlantic have depths of 13,740 ft. and 12,254 ft., respectively.

The geographical extent of these strange events includes not only Siberia and Alaska, but northern portions of Asia, Europe, and North America. The remains of extinct species of mammoths, rhinoceros, horses, oxen and large quadrupeds are linked by dating methods to one single event. Walt Brown quotes Sir Henry Howorth (page 236, Brown) as stating:

*"The instances of the soft parts of the great pachyderms being preserved are not mere local and sporadic ones, but they form a long chain of examples along the whole length of Siberia, from the Urals to the land of the Chukchis (the Bering Strait), so that we have to do here with a condition of things which prevails, and with meteorological conditions that extend over a continent.*

*"When we find such a series ranging so widely, preserved in the same perfect way, and all evidencing a sudden change of climate from a comparatively temperate one to one of great rigor, we cannot help concluding that they all bear witness to a common event. We cannot postulate a separate climate*

*cataclysm for each individual case and each individual locality, but we are forced to the conclusion that the now permanently frozen zone in Asia became frozen at the same time from the same cause."*

Howorth's statement is a grand summation and undeniable evidence that a single, sudden, horrible event occurred on a global scale. Walt Brown definitely provides the reason with his hydroplate theory. This paper further postulates that a trigger is required to release the subterranean waters and also shift the Earth's crust and mantle as one unit, moving Siberia northward to drastically change its climate. That trigger is a celestial intruder which provided external electromagnetic forces to move the Earth's mantle.

Walt Brown and I differ on where all the extra water came for the Great Deluge. He believes all the water came from subterranean water under the hydroplates. This author supports the belief that the water rose quickly by both the released SCW and the sliding of major portions of East Antarctica's ice sheet into the sea, including an additional slower sea rise by the melting of the northern ice sheets. I certainly do not wish to discredit Brown's theory – but only desire to enhance it and add more stages to this cataclysmic event. Some of Brown's extensive analysis of the evidence on the ground is explored.

## 2. Analysis of *Rock Ice*

(Page 236, Brown) Scientists have found a strange type of ice in and under the muck containing mammoth remains. Tolmachoff, a Russian researcher called it *rock ice*. It is identified by having a yellow tinge and contains rounded and elongated bubbles. This rock ice has a granular structure on the surface that can be easily rubbed off with your hand. It looks and feels like compacted hail. Brown compares rock ice with the three generic types of ice. The rock ice compares more closely to many small drops of water freezing while moving rapidly through cold air. Examples are hail, sleet and windblown spray. But rock ice differs from all the generic ices by having many large bubbles, the highest bubble content of 16 %; no dissolved air; having a yellow tinge due to a chemical reaction when exposed with air; and having easily-seen embedded dirt and plant particles.

Brown proves his point that had this water frozen in a normal way, the dirt would have settled out and the vegetable matter would have floated upward. Obviously, the rock ice was never part of a lake or stream. This ice, unlike all normal ices, did not have saturated air, concluding that the hydroplate ejection caused water to go high above the atmosphere, where it froze without significant air being present. According to frozen-food experts, mammoths were preserved in such a way that the outer layers of skin would have had to drop suddenly at least -150 to -175 °F (page 236, Brown). Brown deduces that some type of heat sink would need to be even colder to explain these extreme cold temperatures in the middle of the Siberian summer season. The only possibility is for this heat sink to occur above the atmosphere while water moved through the airless stratosphere and froze. Hence, Brown's theory of the hydroplates is well constructed and corroborated.

## 3. Evidence versus Theories for Frozen Mammoths

(p. 244, Table 12, Brown) Various other theories are analyzed by Brown in his table for "Evidence vs. Theories: Frozen Mammoths". The other theories are presented, besides the hydroplate and the shifting crust/mantle, to explain frozen mammoths. They are lake drownings, crevasses, mud burial, river transport, extinction by man, the Bering Strait barrier preventing the warmth of Pacific waters, mild ice age and a meteorite impact. All these other theories certainly can explain certain types of deaths, but never for these discoveries of frozen and buried mammoths over an entire range of landscape with such simultaneous and sudden fury.

The extensive evidence is listed in Brown's table as being:

1.  abundant and types of food not being available in such cold climates

2.  warm climates required for such buried flora and fauna including that found in the stomachs of frozen mammoths

3.  numerous discovered deaths away from rivers, ruling out river flooding

4.  yedomas, or strange hills, 30 to 260 feet high, containing both materials predicted by the hydroplate theory and containing herds of buried mammoths

5.  elevated burials on high plateaus where animals sought less dust and muck

6.  mammoth bone and ivory on Arctic islands that washed there after the flood receded

7.  involvement of these particular kinds of death over large geographical areas of Asia, Europe, and North America

8.  rock ice previously explained **only** by the hydroplate theory

9.  frozen muck or fine sediments in muddy rain and ice mixed with pulverized vegetation surrounding burials

10. sudden freezing, down to -150 °F, to stop destructive activity of enzymes and stomach acids and preserve mammoth flesh

11. suffocation analyzed in many deaths

12. dirty lungs and digestive tracts containing silt, clay and small gravel, emphasizing the fierce strong winds and laden filled atmosphere

13. mostly the larger, stronger animal remains were discovered, unlike the smaller animals that were impossible to preserve in such turmoil

14. sudden deaths were mostly determined to occur in the summer-fall seasons, ruling out a sudden extreme climatic change

15. mixes of animal bones of both prey and predator were found together, even inside caves

16. upright and vertically compressed carcasses of both frozen and skeletal mammoths were found.

This is my conclusion: only taken together can the hydroplate theory and crustal/mantle-shift hypothesis adequately address all these enigmas of the frozen mammoths. Since Brown rules against a crustal/mantle shift occurring because he never considers any cause, such as the close encounter of another celestial body and its electrical/magnetic interaction. He imagines an *Earth Roll* that shifted the entire Earth by about 30° due to an imbalance of the uplifted mountains, collapsed hydroplates and an almost immediate continental drift away from the mid-Atlantic ridge. This Earth Roll idea is faulty thinking on Brown's part, having no geophysical credibility.

Of course, one can also question crustal/mantle shifting; however, more inductive reasoning and scientific evidence follows to support this idea. There is less gyroscopic spinning stability and reduced rotational energy to change for a crustal/mantle shift, compared with the entire Earth; and, there is a less massive mantle riding on a clutch-like inner core fluid boundary. Further supporting indications for a crustal/mantle shift are:

1. the continuing climatic changes such as in Siberia.

2. the polar location changes that resulted in the melting of the Laurentide Ice Sheet.

3. the continuing permafrost in Siberia.

4.  the sliding of the East Antarctic Ice Sheet into the ocean.

5.  the almost simultaneous releases of the hydroplate ejecta and increased volcanism, due to needed adjustments of the Earth's geoid.

6.  the direct evidence of the Earth's past spin axis location using the measured wandering magnetic poles and,

7.  the recent evidence gathered by space probes about how other planets in the solar system are magnetically and electrically disrupted.

## C. SIBERIAN CLIMATE AND GEOLOGY

### 1. Why Did Siberia Become Cold So Quickly?

The most commonly occurring climate in Siberia is subarctic, with an annual average temperature of about 23°F and an average for January of -13°F.[53] Most of the land, especially above the Arctic Circle, is permafrost, having only a few species of trees that can survive. Soils give way to an active layer that becomes thicker, and the ice content is lower, in the southern flatter regions of Siberia. Rich grasslands that formed the original vegetation of the southern plains are now non-existent.[54] Certainly, extinct grazing animals, such as mammoths, rhinoceros and certain species of horses, could never thrive now in this climate and on this vegetation, yet here is where the remains of herds of these animals are buried and frozen. Immense piles of large temperate trees are found in these same regions. Obviously, a dramatic climatic change occurred. Why? The postulated reason is that the crustal/mantle unit moved rather quickly about 30° of latitude northward, toward the north pole, from a temperate climate that easily supported this megafauna, larger trees and rich grasslands. The quickness of the cold and burial in muck are explained by the hydroplate theory, causing the rapid precipitation of frozen $CO_2$, hail and muck, jetting from deep subterranean pressurized chambers under the Arctic Ocean.

### 2. Yedomas[55]

*Yedomas* (p. 237, Brown) is a Russian term for frequently occurring hills, 30 to 260 feet high, which many times became cemeteries for herds of mammoths, other grazing animals and mature forests. Yedomas are honeycombed with ice, suggesting that high winds accompanied the deposition that probably had a fairly uniform thickness, sometimes having unbelievable heights of 260 feet. Water collected in depressions and over thousands of years of summer melting created these hills. Walt Brown exemplifies the ferocity of these Siberian storms during the Great Deluge in the following quoted text (page 238, Brown). *"Sometimes the ice, which several Russian geologists have concluded was formed simultaneously with the soil, accounts for 90% of the yedoma's volume. Some yedomas contain broken trees in the wildest disorder. The natives call them 'wood hills' and the buried trees 'Noah's wood.' Yedoma soil is similar to muck. It contains tiny plant remains, is high in salt and carbonate and has more than two and a half times the carbon that is in all the world's tropical forests!"* This enigma of the yedomas begs for an answer, which Brown provides.

### 3. Loess Soils

*Loess* (p. 238, Brown), a fertile soil that is also rich in carbonates, has a yellow tinge caused by the oxidation of iron-bearing minerals after deposition. The remains of extinct animals of the Holocene transition are frequently found in these soils. These soils lack internal layering and cover and are found at various elevations in large regions such as Alaska, central United States, northern China and Siberia. The Yellow River and Yellow Sea received their name from the suspended particles of this soil. It is believed these deposits were spread under windblown and cold glacial conditions. However, Siberia, except for the extreme western portion, was never glaciated. Animals were frozen and buried quickly enough in this layer of soil to prevent significant decay or mutilation by scavengers. What, in the name of God, happened? Again, Brown's hydroplates address another enigma of the loess soils. Please be reminded that the loess depositions occur mostly in the northern temperate latitudes. This author suggests the origin is mostly from the ripped apart oceanic ridges of the northern seas, especially the Arctic, when the crustal/mantle layer was suddenly yanked apart by magnetic forces.

### 4. The Push and Pull of Magnetic Force of an Overhead Celestial Body

As previously mentioned, the initiating magnetic forces for moving the entire crustal/mantle unit of Earth began in the northern polar region. The initial pull ripped apart the Arctic Ocean's ridge which created the maximum release of the pressurized water under the hydroplates. The initial push or force in the opposite direction caused much lifting and folding of existing mountain ranges in North and South America. An excellent example of the push force or horizontal compression of a mountain range is the Buckled Mountain near the Sullivan River in southern British Columbia, Canada. A very compelling picture of this horizontal buckling process is shown in Brown's book on page 112. The repeated folding is almost vertical, like a carpet being crumpled together against a wall. This crumpling and folding of mountain ranges is found repeatedly and globally, showing the presence of strong horizontal forces along any crustal region that was weakened already by mountain building processes. The electrical and magnetic forces formed initially along the crustal surface, and then were transferred through the Moho layer, or crust-to-mantle transition, into the deeper mantle to displace, as a unit, the entire globe of crust and mantle, simultaneously.

The initial magnetic pull forces in the northern polar regions stretched the Siberian land mass northward, being roughly directed between the 90° East and the 75° East meridians. This land mass remained mostly flat, with no new uplifting and folding of mountain ranges. After the surface forces were transferred to the mantle and the globally encompassing magnetic field permeated deeply enough, the connection of the mantle to the outer liquid iron core was decoupled briefly to cause a 30° shift in latitude southward along the 75° East meridian line and northward along the 105° West. Other planets in our solar system show similar displacements between their spin axis and magnetic dipole axis. Most likely, the reasons for the displacements of these immense masses is similar.

Because the Earth is spinning from west to east, horizontal forces are created in the crust, which is separated from the upper mantle by the Moho transition zone. When the crust and mantle moved along a meridian line, vector forces on the crust combined from two separate directions: the direction of spin and a direction perpendicular to the spin, as the crust/mantle unit moved southward in the Western Hemisphere and northward in the Eastern Hemisphere for 30 degrees of latitude. The dynamic resultant forces caused a separate shifting of the crust above the Moho toward an easterly direction, to create the uplifting of the tectonic plates at their weakest point along the edges. The Ring of Fire, or a ring of very volcanic mountainous ranges, surrounding the Pacific Ocean basin was created. The thicker, lighter continental plates of North America and South America were pushed over top the easterly movement of the thinner and heavier oceanic plates of the Pacific and Nazca Plates. These oceanic plates, in turn, being thinner and heavier were pushed under the easterly movement of the thicker and lighter continental plates of the Eurasia, Filipino, Australian Plates and the western part of the North American Plate. This pushing of the lighter continental crusts over the heavier oceanic crusts caused serious buckling as is witnessed by very deep oceanic trenches and the sinking of major island chains in the eastern Pacific. Direct evidence of this dramatic uplifting of mountains is given by the existence of a pre-deluge advanced civilization along an ocean coastline that was lifted 10,000 to 12,000 feet in elevation in the Andes Mountains of Bolivia and Peru. More information is given later.

# XI.

# COMPENDIUM OF DATA SUPPORTING THE GREAT DELUGE

## A. THE COSMIC CATASTROPHE 11,500 YEARS BP

It is time to introduce an excellent book about the Great Deluge by D.S. Allan and J.B. Delair. Allan, a Cambridge M.A., is a science historian specializing in paleogeography, particularly in the Arctic regions. Delair is an Oxford-based geologist and anthropologist with much field experience. In 1995, they published a "must-read" book, *Cataclysm! Compelling Evidence of a Cosmic Catastrophe in 9500 B.C.*[56] The book is a multi-disciplinary, scientific study – one of the first to make a serious attempt of overcoming the paradigm that the Great Deluge is merely a myth or legend.

Unlike Walt Brown, for Allan and Delair, celestial visitors caused all of Earth's calamity during this event. The largest of several passing cosmic bodies caused immense electrical, magnetic and gravitational disturbances. Another smaller body was caught by the Earth's gravitational field, broke apart after passing through the Roche limit and fell to Earth, causing fire storms, tsunamis and a rain of stony debris and ice. Like Brown, an attendance of many types of calamities occurred and ended, with the most remembered and most recorded being global flooding. For Allan and Delair, the celestial destroyer was called *Phaeton*, which after creating more havoc for the planet, Venus, crashed into the Sun. The legacy of this cataclysm, according to Allan and Delair, was to drive mankind's well-developed civilizations of the Golden Age into the Stone Age and create the Holocene mass extinction. This conclusion directly counters accepted dogma of mankind's evolving onward from a Stone Age mentality during that time.

## B. THE CAUSES AND TYPES OF SO MUCH CALAMITY

This encounter with cometary-type celestial bodies led to many global catastrophes that are very similar to what this paper envisions happening when one of the brown dwarf star's entourage had a close encounter. Some basic and very important differences are listed:

1. The intruding celestial bodies did not come from a distant star, such as the Vega Supernova, as predicted by Allan and Delair; the intruders are a brown dwarf star system that makes a lengthy (so far undetected) orbit around the Sun every 3600 years. Yes, if you do the math, this brown dwarf has visited our inner solar system three other times since the Great Deluge, creating havoc each time, but not as serious as during the Great Deluge event. However, like Allan and Delair and this paper, the magnetic properties and electrical potential, along with gravitational forces, all strongly influenced the interaction of this close encounter with Earth.

2. For Allan and Delair, the Earth's spin axis was altered by at least 30° with respect to the ecliptic, thereby changing the geoid slightly due to tidal acceleration forces. For this paper, only the crust and mantle shifted as one unit on the liquid inner core, permanently changing the geoid dramatically, by giving new locations on the crust for the equator and poles. The centrifugal force of rotation made these changes.

3. The flooding primarily came from the "heaping" of seas and lakes, flowing off raised or sinking land masses, due to dynamic forces created by the slowing of Earth; giant tides due to Phaeton's gravitational attraction; and additionally, from the melting of a smaller comet that fell to Earth as hail and liquid rain. The waters for this paper came from the Eastern Antarctica Ice Sheet sliding off a land mass into the ocean, the rapid melting of the northern Laurentide Ice Sheet and the explosive release of supercritical water from Walt Brown's subterranean hydroplates.

Allan and Delair certainly compiled a long list of convincing evidences for the calamities that followed their supposed cosmic encounter in the following disciplines of: geography, geology, biology, paleontology and geophysics. The following geophysical changes that are dated to have occurred during the "late Pleistocene" times or, in other words, the Younger Dryas geological period are tabulated for each continental region. They are the: formation of deserts; dried-up rivers, lakes and seas; disappearance of land-bridges and land masses; raised beaches; increased volcanism; over-thrusting of older over younger strata; crustal tilting and folding; lateral crustal displacement; sea floor collapse; sunken plateaus; and elevation changes. How could all these global manifestations occur over a very short period unless there was a shift in the crust and mantle as a unit, caused by a sudden change to the Earth's geoid? There is no other explanation. Changing the spin axis, as Allan and Delair postulate, is not the answer, because the pole locations would not have changed; however, it does address long term changing climates. The slowing of the Earth envisioned by Allan and Delair does address geoid changes, since the centrifugal forces are reduced to create a slight compression and sinking of the crustal plates, but it does not answer how the oceanic ridges were pulled apart to release subterranean waters. These processes of Earth slowing and tilting would require too much external energy being applied in unknown ways, with the resulting heat energy causing both frying of the land surfaces and boiling of the oceans, which obviously did not happen. There were survivors. The amount of energy to tilt the Earth would obviously create forces to obliterate the planet. The mass of the Earth's mantle is two thirds of the mass of the entire Earth, which makes changing the mantle's rotation for a very brief time much more probable than tilting the entire mass of Earth. The ease of rotation is provided by the almost frictionless liquid gimbal of the outer core of the Earth.

To further corroborate the crustal/mantle shift, Allan and Delair (p. 67) are quoted. *"Extraordinary accumulations of incompatible organisms – shells, birds, mammals, plants and so on – were encountered in 'drift' deposits hundreds, even thousands, of miles too far north of their present habitats. _ _ _ _ Elsewhere, extensive debris of ancient forests were met with in northern lands now far too cold to support any such vegetation, yet the immense ice-sheets of conventional Ice Age dogma had somehow avoided them and failed to scour away their trunks and branches as it had allegedly scoured away rocks elsewhere when accumulating the 'drift' deposits. _ _ _ _ at variance with inescapable field evidence, that the standard notion of the Ice Age must now be regarded as fundamentally flawed and almost certainly a chimera."*

Allan and Delair suspected that the large ice sheets of the northern hemisphere did not exist, since they lack a mechanism like a latitudinal crustal/mantle shift to displace the north pole from the Hudson Bay/northern Quebec region, center of the Laurentide Ice Sheet, to its present location in the middle of the Arctic Ocean. It is very conceivable, if the pre-deluge north pole was on the North American land mass, that an ice cap could form there just like the one presently in Antarctica. Also, the Siberian coastal regions could then grow rich grasslands supporting megafauna, and Axel Heiberg and Ellsmere Islands in northern Canada could possibly support animals and plants that can only now live in temperate climates, similar to today's coastal forests of Oregon. Yes, Allan and Delair have undeniable evidence for a catastrophic crustal/mantle shift, but have chosen the wrong model of a total spin axis shift or tilt. The forces required for a spin axis shift or tilt by another celestial body, overcoming a very stable gyroscopic-like angular momentum, would be so great that almost certain thermal and physical destruction of both bodies would occur. And, since Allan and

Delair have the wrong model, they give no consideration for the south pole's making a drastic corresponding latitudinal location change and dislodging the Antarctica Ice Sheet from its landmass.

A brief depiction of the destruction is given in the same outline form as in Allan and Delair's book (pp. 241-317). The authors portray many different multi-culture ancient myths to account for each of their portrayals. The matching of so-called ancient myths with what is found in the real world by these authors is absolutely fantastic. This accounting of these myths from every continent will persuade you to consider that these very-believable stories were passed down from the few lucky survivors and are, indeed, not in the realm of legends or surreal imaginations. The traditions and sagas of ancient peoples become believable in their own right.

## 1. The World Before the Flood

The antediluvian world (p. 241, Allan and Delair) was the legendary *Golden Age* that had a long span of geological stability and a proliferation of plant and animal life, even in latitudes that are now polar. The biological evidence indicates that Earth's climate was more genial with longer days and fewer seasonal changes. The land and sea dispositions were different with more land bridges. Mountains were lower; perhaps seas were shallower. Deserts and ice sheets were less extensive with northern Canada, Alaska and Western Antarctica giving evidence of pre-existing temperate climates. This paper asserts that the Golden Age did exist, and Earth at that time had a different equator and poles. The resulting ice caps stored much more water, making sea level much lower. The climates, winds and sea currents were very different. In a similar fashion, Allan and Delair reason that these same attributes are due to the past Earth's tilt being more perpendicular to its orbit. A little later, it will be learned that the Electric Universe scientific community attributes the Golden Age to a much more radical, perhaps somewhat more plausible reason.

## 2. The Interactions of Electromagnetism and Gravity

The stages of confrontation (p. 250, Allan and Delair) for the cosmic intruders are quite similar for Allan and Delair and this paper. There is the gravitational interaction, causing unusual upheavals of tides for both sea and land. There are the violent electromagnetic exchanges, resulting in high-energy discharge of plasma between the bodies, appearing as a large tongue, or mountain, in the north polar region, connecting the two planets. The Earth was electrified and magnetized along rivers and seacoasts, which released severe lightning bolts, causing immense sputtering of land materials and starting major conflagration of plant life. The electric currents touched down in the north polar region of Earth and traveled southward, centered along the 75° W meridian line. The atmosphere became filled with debris caused by the sputtering of this continuous plasma arc's striking the Earth's surface. The sputtering of this giant electric arc splattered into the atmosphere not only rock/gravel and water, but ices from the ice sheet, and also methane, accumulated in reservoirs within the crust. Allan and Delair attributed the fallen debris from the sky to an asteroid, traveling with Phaeton, that approached the Roche Limit and exploded into millions of pieces which fell to Earth. This scenario is quite possible, but does not adequately explain ice, methane, gravel and sand falling from the sky as is described by the authors.

## 3. Fallen Sky and Prolonged Darkness

Allan and Delair give very descriptive and particular credence to the topics of:

1. plasma arc discharges predicted by the Electric Universe community

2. Walt Brown's idea of hydroplates

3. the huge buildup of magnetization in the Earth's crust and mantle that quickly shifts crust and mantle - in the following quoted paragraph (p. 258, Allan and Delair): *"Celestial electromagnetic exchanges of the size and frequency suggested must also have generated electrical currents not only on Earth's surface but also deeper, selecting metalliferous (better conducting) strata, following metallic veins — perhaps to great depths with the crust — and producing huge thermal increases worldwide. Repeated discharges on this scale would quickly generate sufficient heat to cause: almost instantaneous expansion of the water naturally locked up in crustal strata, resulting in extensive fissuring and splitting of surface rocks; the upwards flow of magna from the deeper fissures; and the activation of volcanoes. Oceans and seas would have boiled and steamed. In combination, these disturbances would, through a general release of heat, smoke, and dust, initiate atmospheric pollution that would last for decades."*

Intense volcanism is known to exist at the end of Pleistocene period. Enormous eruptions by the hundreds occurred during this late Quaternary age, almost simultaneously, especially in the Aleutians, Andes, Antarctica and Iceland. This attests to simultaneous global crustal disturbances and to the tremendous volcanic ash and $CO_2$ poured into the atmosphere. The weight of the polluted atmosphere forced the cloud base down to very low levels, causing unprecedented local electrical storms. The Sun's rays were blocked, causing the cooler conditions that created the postulated beginning of the Younger Dryas period, about 12,900 years BP. Radiocarbon dating of this period, because of the overload of $CO_2$ from volcanism and hydroplate ejections, caused the $C^{14}/C^{12}$ ratio to be much lower, thereby making organic specimens appear much older. The hydroplate water and deeper, older melting of ice sheets also created a reservoir of water that indicated a lower, older ratio of $C^{14}/C^{12}$. What actually happened is that the Younger Dryas was kicked off by the cosmic intruder that created the Great Deluge and the global cooling effect, which then took hundreds of years for recovery. This recovery included the refreezing of ice sheets, sea level to drop to present level and for the atmosphere to cleanse itself of dust and other contaminants. So, the Younger Dryas probably lasted about 11,500 years BP to 10,000 years BP, when Earth's recovery took place, as opposed to the current thinking of 12,900 to 11,500 years BP.

## 4. Earth's Crust Ruptures

Because adjustments to the Earth's geoid took place when the mantle shifted, the lithosphere fractured, due to either compression or stretching. This process caused faulting; earthquakes; rising and lowering plateaus; mountain uplifts and folding; sea and lake bottoms rising and dumping their waters; and the opening of oceanic ridges to release waters from the 'Deep'.

Allan and Delair have the tendency to believe these crustal disturbances (p. 262), which certainly are recorded as happening, were the result of tidal pulls, slowing the Earth's rotation and tilting the spin axis. These processes would require too much external energy and resulting heat build-up that would fry land surfaces and boil the oceans, which obviously did not happen.

## 5. Global Conflagrations

The first conflagrations were caused by plasma arcing from the celestial visitor in the north polar region and subsequent streaming of high-voltage electric currents southward along the Earth's surface, especially along a certain range of meridian degrees. As the crust almost immediately started adjusting to the shifted mantle, severe volcanism was initiated, causing hot ejecta to rain down and flammable gases to escape from seismic fissures. Large grasslands and forests perished rapidly by burning.

An interesting scenario was a legendary account of falling burning fluids (p. 269, Allan and Delair). These fluids can only be hydrocarbons, dredged from certain crustal locations by the cutting and gouging of super high-energy plasma arcing striking the Earth's crust. Hydrocarbons could also have been released by the hydroplates that, when falling to Earth, caught on fire by either existing surface fires or volcanic ash released high into the atmosphere.

## 6. Abounding Hurricanes and Tornadoes

Because Earth's geoid changed rapidly within hours or perhaps a few days, the Coriolis effect of the global weather cells, the changing ocean currents and the dramatic electrical effects on the atmosphere caused winds of hurricane proportions. The evidence is seen in boulder/clay matrix spread out over large regions, having a uniform sheet that filled up valleys and depressions, and was thin or absent on the tops of higher ground. There are also the previously mention *drifts*, deposited under violent conditions, that affected vast areas simultaneously. I now succumb to the elegant description (p. 277) by Allan and Delair of these fierce winds creating drifts of a tumultuous appearance, especially in the northern polar regions.

*"The 'boulder clay' was almost certainly viscous when first deposited. Prior to attaining that consistency, however, it had existed on the original land surface as sand and soil particles which, from the earliest stages of the catastrophe onwards, were frequently disturbed by lightning strikes and heavily augmented by prodigious falls of volcanic ash and dust produced by the ever-increasing volcanism. Super-cyclonic winds subsequently whirled up all this material from the pre-catastrophic landscape, depositing it as a great dusty mantle over hill and dale alike. Shortly afterwards it was converted into a great muddy paste by the Deluge waters which redistributed it tumultuously where we now find it. As we shall soon see, the Deluge was not long in materializing and apparently commenced its activities well before the super-winds were eventually dissipated. It was the combination of water and wind which bodily moved the 'drift' across the convulsed landscape. That much of the 'drift' was deposited in this manner is indicated by the presence in it, in many places, of upright tree stumps with their roots still firmly embedded in the original soils underlying the 'drift'. These stumps protrude upwards into the basal layers of the 'drift'. Had ice deposited the 'drift', then these stumps would have been obliterated. They were not."*

Allan and Delair, as well as this author, are definitely convinced that much disaster occurred a short time previous to the Deluge. However, we differ in where the inventory of water came from to create the Deluge, especially since they do not believe in the extent of large ice sheets during that time. The claim that some waters for the Deluge came from the release of pressurized water from subterranean chambers, such as is described best by Walt Brown, is accepted by Allan and Delair and this author. But this author claims that much more water came in two slow surges, the first being the rapid melting of the northern ice sheets and then, secondly, the slipping into the ocean of significant amounts of the East Antarctica Ice Sheet.

## 7. Barrage of Falling Objects

Allan and Delair's strongest suggestion for the cause of bombardments is meteorites that accompanied their celestial visitor, Phaeton. Some of their cited evidence is the *Carolina bays* situated along the coastal areas of South and North Carolina and Georgia, with areas of abundant meteorite discoveries in adjacent areas. These Carolina bays are of particular interest because they are dated to the Late Pleistocene period. These so-called bays, numbering more than 140,000, are mostly elliptical depressions, with variations of round and oval shapes and sizes. The remarkable feature about these high-density occurring depressions is that they run parallel to each other in a north-west to south-east direction (pp. 281-289, Allan and Delair).

Other similar geological features occur in Northern Alaska, the Old Crow Plain in the Yukon Territory and the Beni Basin in Bolivia, but with little dating data. Their appearances on the surface, using aerial photographs, indicates probably Pleistocene to recent times. Curiously, no mention is made of looking for meteorites buried in these crater-looking depressions. This author wishes to address other reasons for bombardments of large objects, keeping in mind that previously mentioned erratic boulders found randomly throughout the world must be accounted for, too.

The explosive release of pressurized supercritical water at oceanic ridges described by Walt Brown and the initiation of extinct and new volcanoes would also have launched projectiles to cause an uncountable series of severe bombardments. However, the bombardment described by the Caroline bays and the Beni Basin in Bolivia more than likely came from terrestrial icy rocks that were sputtered skyward by the gigantic plasma arcing in the northern polar regions of Earth during its close encounter with a rogue planet. This sputtering, on a commercial industrial scale, is like laser welding that cuts through metal. The ejecta from a sputtered crust and ice sheet can be envisioned at times as being highly directional, spatially very dense and made of a certain varying range of rocky objects. Likely, a meteorite fall could not cause the high density of impacts seen in the Carolina bays; the broken pieces of a meteorite would be spread over a much longer distance with much less density.

It is clearly not hard to imagine the following scenario of the initial contact of a high energy electrical arcing from the passing highly-charged rogue planet. The huge Birkland currents from this rogue were magnetically attracted to the Earth's pre-deluge north pole, located in the Hudson Bay region. The Hudson Bay was gouged away and rocks were propelled, mostly in southerly directions, to produce the world's enigmatic erratic boulders. Possibly, one last principal arc discharge created the James Bay, directly south of Hudson Bay. Looking at a globe, one will find, coincidentally, that James Bay is strangely aligned with the Carolina bay region and the longer axis of their oblong shapes. Both rocks from James Bay bedrock and chunks of ice from the Laurentide Ice Sheet were surely the culprits of this unusual bombardment.

## 8. Traces of Heavy Metals

An iridium layer found in sediments dated 26 million years ago is supposedly from a meteorite impact that caused the dinosaur extinction event. In a similar fashion, Allan and Delair have identified red-brown tints or traces of iron and iron oxide on numerous geological young deposits. In particular, iron and manganese staining are found with Younger Dryas drift deposits. A rusty color is also characteristic of late Pleistocene loess formations of that same period. The silica and heavy mineral grains found in these loessic deposits consist mostly of fresh and angular types that signify its recent age. How do heavy metals find their way into surface deposits that also contain animal and plant remains? (p. 294, Allan and Delair) Simply, only two answers are possible. The more probable answer is of terrestrial origin, where these heavy metals were mined deep in the crust, melted and blasted into the atmosphere by the plasma arcing between Earth and a rogue planet. The destructiveness of this high-energy plasma arcing was on a planetary scale beyond any believable human experience. The other answer is that heavy metal ions were brought along with the Birkland currents from the rogue planet and finely distributed throughout Earth's atmosphere before settling to the surface.

## 9. Magnetic Spherules of Nickel and Iron

Again, Allan and Delair are cited in making an original claim that the myriads of small, black, nickel-rich magnetic spherules, having diameters from 10 to 50 microns, found globally on all ocean bottoms are due to the Deluge event. Also, covering the ocean floors are red clay of oxidized ferric iron particles with manganese oxide (p. 297, Allan and Delair). Other authorities have theorized meteorite origins or slow growth through natural chemical accretion. The slow-growth theory is nullified due to these clays and nodules overlying geologically young lavas and basalts, making them even more youthful. Allan and Delair declare that these nodules were dumped all at once, rather than accumulating slowly. This dumping is referred to "the rains of death" and is responsible for a widespread loss of marine life which was discovered in the sediments of the eastern Atlantic. The dating of these marine organisms was sometime between 14,000 to 11,000 years BP, which squarely marks the end of the last ice age.

This author's opinion is that "the rains of death" denotes several possible scenarios with regard to the idea of an immense plasma arcing occurring at the north polar region and subsequently producing violent electrical currents running southerly, through highly conductive oceans, toward the opposite electrical dipole at the South Pole.

1. The high energy arcing process of removing materials for creating the Hudson Bay could have mined, melted and blasted liquid iron, nickel and manganese into the atmosphere. There are presently large deposits of nickel being mined south of Hudson Bay in the Sudbury region of Canada.

2. The arcing process on the rogue planet launched large crustal chunks that were caught in the Earth's gravitational field and began orbiting Earth. This sputtered orbiting debris eventually slowed enough to enter the Roche limit and burn and annihilate into smaller pieces, including nodules.

3. Or, the cruising electrical current or traversing lightning bolts sought more highly conductive veins of metallic elements within the oceanic crust, melting and jettisoning these materials into the water above, where they rapidly cooled into nodules and fine grains that then returned to the ocean bottom. Since the Earth's crust and mantle developed a very strong magnetic field, the solidifying nodules became magnetized. The element radium became mixed with the other heavy metals and made the nodules radioactive.

This author has a strong preference, using only deductive reasoning, for the above three scenarios as opposed to an entourage of cometary bodies envisioned by Allan and Delair following Phaeton and breaking apart and then crashing into Earth. The entry of asteroids or cometary bodies into the atmosphere should normally break them into big chunks that fall rapidly, preventing any type of even distribution throughout the Earth's oceans as is seen by the spherules and nodules of nickel and iron.

## 10. Raised Oceans and Seas

The reason for the *water mountain* or the Great Deluge is not well explained by Allan and Delair, since they lack the necessary water inventory, such as melting extremely glaciated polar ice caps and the estimated full extent of the hydroplate reservoirs. Their estimates for the maximum rise in sea level are anywhere from the Biblical statement of 15 cubits estimated to be 23 feet or as high as some of the tallest mountains (p. 301, Allan and Delair). They categorize the sources of water as:

1. The heaping and spilling over of raised oceans and seas, due to geoid re-alignments and changing tidal forces. However, no actual geoid adjustment can take place if the interaction of Phaeton, according to Allan and Delair, changed the tilt of the Earth and slowed its rotation. If this process indeed occurred, then it is possible for dynamic forces to heap water, similar to sloshing water in a large pan. The slowing of Earth's rotation and/or the tilt of the spin axis are considered to be physically impossible by this author. The energies required would either result in the obliteration of Earth or raise surface temperature enough to boil away all the oceans.

2. A torrent of cosmic origin is also given, which is never really explained. They are apparently trying to respond to the Noah story of 40 days and 40 nights of rain.

3. The combination of the united terrestrial and cosmic waters produces the water mountain. For this author, although I am impressed with all their gathered evidence for a catastrophe and flood 11,500 years BP, Allan and Delair fail to provide a convincing argument for the source(s) of the building water mountain or the deluge of ocean waters.

## 11. Waters from the Deep

Again, Allan and Delair miss the most important point: where did the water come from and where did it go? They weakly attributed that icy cometary bodies followed Phaetons' path, and then were caught in Earth's gravity field, to eventually melt while in orbit and fall as rain and snow. If Phaeton supposedly had interactions with other planets in the solar system before coming close to Earth, Phaeton would have certainly shed its entourage of volatile bodies that had much less mass. Also, the study of isotopic water on Earth reveals no cosmic origins. Finally, since their book was written, space probes have definitely proven that both comets and asteroids are waterless. Walt Brown's long-lived torrent coming from the Deep, or immense hydroplate reservoirs inside subterranean chambers, does make more sense. The waters from the Deep freezing high above the atmosphere and falling as hail and muck also corroborates and supports the frozen mammoth event.

## 12. The Great Deluge

The Deluge, by many natural historians, is thought to be local flooding caused by tsunamis, storm surges, immense river flooding coming from ice dam breaks or inland seas rising due to rising oceans overflowing connecting straits. Tsunami waves can have heights of 100 feet and one was recorded in Alaska to have reached a height of 1700 feet by swashing up a mountain side. However, even the largest tsunami waves are not capable of travelling very far inland. None of these mechanisms can address global flooding. Allan and Delair attempt to address the Deluge by geoidal shape-changes coming from the slowing and tilting of the Earth. The slowing of the Earth can only reduce the centrifugal forces for expanding the oblate shape of the Earth. Water running off raised seas will not happen. If indeed, the whole Earth tilted, then the location of poles and equator would not change with respect to the rotation. Only mild changes in the average sea level would take place due tidal acceleration forces because different parts of the Earth are now closer to both the Moon and Sun due to the tilting axis. Geoidal deformation did take place, but not by Allan and Delair's accounting.

Allan and Delair cite some interesting memories by the Choctaw tribe in Oklahoma and the Navajos of the Southwest. Their ancestors describe a bright white wall proceeding toward them, which was really an advancing watery wave. For the Navajo, these walls on the horizon came from different directions. These waters were probably the combination of ice dams breaking within the Laurentide ice sheet to the north and the bottoms of inland lakes and seas being uplifted, causing the overflow of their waters. Since the underlying crust of these lands shifted southward due to the mantle shifting, the geoidal shape would have raised resulting in a massive run-off of water.

So, yes, local flooding on each continent would occur near the same time, but then the overall sea level would steadily rise due the continuing melting of the Laurentide and other northern ice sheets. Some dramatic surges would occur a little later as the East Antarctica Ice Sheet calved and/or slid off the land into the southern seas. Allan and Delair's concept of the seas heaping up can only be very transient. This author's idea is that the post-global flood waters persisted for perhaps hundreds of years, while the water inventory adjusted to rebuilding ice sheets in Antarctica, Greenland and mountains that were raised to greater altitudes. Also, great amounts of water would be gathered by the new permafrost regions of Alaska and Siberia.

## 13. Wreckage of the Arctic

The author again submits to another direct quote from Allan and Delair (p. 309). *"Enormous accumulations of sub-fossil and carbonized wood occur along the Arctic shores of Siberia, along the coastline of the Bering Strait, and on various islands both north and south of that channel. Staggering amounts exist on many of the New Siberian Islands and, as we have seen, in the Alaskan 'muck' beds. The vast quantities of vegetable matter represent whole forests which have been obliterated and buried catastrophically. The constituent trees, which include sycamore, poplar, alder and sequoia, today flourish much farther south, and represent a typical Miocene/Pliocene forest assemblage, evidently forming part of that flora which persisted more or less unchanged into Pleistocene times, before being overwhelmed."*

Allan and Delair are simply providing more testament that global catastrophe struck not only the mammoth and other fauna, but also the flora of northern polar regions across the entire top of Asia and North America. By now, most readers can agree that a catastrophe on grand proportions did occur, but the important point is made that these particular types of forests do not thrive at the latitudes where they were found. In fact, these wood hills are found 71° N latitude, well beyond the present northern limit of any trees. Straightforward deduction can only lead you to realize a crustal/mantle displacement had taken place. Allan and Delair's proposed change in the axial tilt of the Earth does not address this anomaly of a persistent and consistent global climate change. If the Earth's spin axis were more perpendicular to the coplanar orbit of Earth around the Sun or the ecliptic plane, then these northern regions would have received a colder climate instead of the temperate one required by these destroyed forests. Another point, not to be overlooked, is how quickly this event occurred. Many trees were found buried still having their leaves and fruit. We can imagine the process taking hours, days and no more than several weeks. More deduction leads one to envision a quickly passing celestial intruder.

How does the wood become carbonized like fossilized charcoal? Obviously, tremendous heat occurred simultaneously with the burial process. The heat came initially from the tremendous radiant energy of the plasma arc discharges striking Earth, that then spread out in all directions, burning forests in its path. The forensics of the Siberian flora and fauna show very convincing evidence for the scenario set forth by this paper.

Allan and Delair reported numerous instances of wood hills, but of particular interest is the fossilized wood found on Ellesmere Island, considered to be of Siberian origin. Ellesmere Island is presently treeless, being about 60° latitude and bordering the frozen Arctic Ocean. This author immediately saw the connection with the crustal/mantle shift of approximately 30°. In antediluvian times, this island was in a high temperature zone, with an ice-free Arctic Ocean between it and Siberia. Plant life and driftwood, at that time, could easily be carried by winds or the ocean waters from Siberia to Ellesmere Island.

### 14. Quick Melting and Quick Freezing

Allan and Delair make a case that the large ice sheets of the northern latitudes (especially the Laurentide) did not exist. The last Ice Age of the Younger Dryas period for them did have an increase of glaciers, but no continuous continental ice sheet covered North America. One of their important claims is that no possible terrestrial conditions are capable of producing enough heat to evaporate immense quantities of water to form such ice sheets. However, they did not realize the possibility of the Laurentide Ice Sheet being centrally located at the pre-deluge north pole. Then, of course, an ice sheet of such large size could form on land in a similar fashion as the Antarctica Ice Sheets. Lacking this concept made Allan and Delair very suspicious, as they well should be, of the Laurentide and Scandinavian Ice Sheets. But, given the crustal/mantle shift concept, the Laurentide becomes very plausible.

Allan and Delair do not stress how so many megafauna species were found fast-frozen, which requires temperatures down to (-170) °F so that their flesh does not putrefy and their inner organs are preserved. They do not have the hydroplate concept that Walt Brown uses. They do not have the crustal/mantle shift concept that quickly changes latitudinal locations on Earth, causing severe climate changes with hurricane winds. Of course, these temperatures are quickly transient and are replaced with normal freezing temperatures. The postdiluvian temperate and equatorial zones of latitude would continue to have colder than normal temperatures for hundreds of years until the atmosphere became clear of dust once again.

## C. ESTABLISHMENT OF PLEISTOCENE/HOLOCENE BOUNDARY

Again, I refer to Allan and Delair's excellent treatment of this subject in their book, *Cataclysm!* They have advocated in their book that a very distinct boundary for the Great Deluge event or the Phaeton disaster, as they called it, is 11,500 years BP. The dating is almost exclusively radiocarbon dating using the $^{14}C/^{12}C$ ratio. The tectonic and hydrological dating was determined by other methods such as Argon-Potassium. Allan & Delair pointed out that A-P dating has its limitations since its half-life is not known and the distribution of Argon is incongruent in rocks and minerals. Many of these specimens were found well-below present ground level. Nevertheless, their compilation of dates and places of finds related to sudden calamity, point directly to this date of 11,500 years BP or 9500 years BC. (pp. 345-348, Appendix B, Allan and Delair)

The organic objects are: botanical specimens, peat deposits and sediments from Europe, Africa, Japan, New Zealand and North America with averages between 11,390 to 11,839 years BP. The zoological objects, both vertebrates and invertebrates, are from Europe, Greenland, Iceland, Siberia, Brazil, Iran and Australia, but mostly clustered in the northern latitudes. Their average dating ranged from 11,564 to 11,670 years BP.

Inorganic geological fines of limestone, carbonates, tufa, dolomite and caliche, found throughout the globe, had average dates of 11,671 to 12,173 years BP. The general average date for the above worldwide specimens is 11,577 years BP. A perfectly preserved deep-frozen baby mammoth was found in 1977. Its death was determined to occur within 14,000 to 9000 years BP, which was assigned on the basis of radiocarbon dates of the general extinction of mammoths in Arctic regions. (p. 343, Allan and Delair)

Geophysical abrupt changes were also compiled, with average dates of 11,125 to 11,600 years BP. Some of these anomalous changes were dramatic rise in water levels, elevation increases, drilled cores with four ash layers, marine transgression, shoreline tilts, unusual temperature changes, warm climate initiation suddenly in Siberia, deglaciation in Alaska, rain forests expanding in Australia, change in sediment source in the Bering Sea, subsidence of the Gulf of Mexico, probably North American inland sea and Rocky Mountain basin lakes drained thereby creating the Grand Canyon, subsidence of the eastern continental shelf of the USA (probably due the collapse of some hydroplates suggested by Walt Brown), glaciers shrinking in Chile, Laurentide ice sheet retreating, end moraines in New Zealand (glaciers retreating due to South Pole relocation) and glaciers disappearing in the Rocky Mountains. (p. 348, Allan & Delair)

Most mainstream scientists agree that something very dramatic occurred on Earth at the end of the Younger Dryas geological period but refuse to speculate. These events taken together are very confusing unless the hypothesis of a worldwide crustal/mantle rotational shift is adopted. The event(s) were very sudden, as attested by deep-frozen mammoths. These scientists are very reluctant, even fearful, to speak-out and make any claims about global catastrophe which includes global flooding. Academia's major paradigms keep them from postulating what triggered such an event and determining where all the water came from and where it went.

# XII.
# ELECTRICITY IN SPACE

Confirmation of what could possibly have happened between a charged celestial body that had a close encounter with Earth is provided by a group of independent scientists that promote the concepts of the Electric Universe, or the EU. Their concepts are summarized in the website, thunderboltsproject.info, and Wallace Thornhill's and David Talbott's book, *The Electric Universe – Volumes 1&2,*[57] among many other EU publications. These two authors have married the disciplines of electrical engineering, plasma technology and comparative mythology into an idea that the electrical and magnetic nature of things, instead of gravity, rules the universe. Their ideas lend direct support that when either an anodic-charged planet or brown dwarf star came close to a negatively-charged planet, Earth, an immense high-energy plasma discharge between the bodies can occur that creates an exchange of charged particles.

## A. BIRKELAND CURRENTS AND ELECTRIC CIRCUITS IN SPACE

One of their hypotheses is that space is filled with plasma (positively-charged ions and negatively-charged electrons) that are in a dark mode or non-glowing state. Plasma that is stressed, due to electrons changing energy levels (by electrons either joining or separating from atoms), will glow, such as is the case of fluorescent lights, auroras on planets, tails of comets and planetary nebula. The Sun and other stars are balls of plasma powered by galactic Birkeland currents. Lightning bolts are narrow channels of plasma with partially ionized atoms and molecules. This lightning has its counterpart in the near-vacuum of space, such as the discharge of plasma between celestial bodies, actually seen by humans in the distant past. Lightning is Earth's attempt to evenly distribute charge and prevent the build-up of too much charge in the atmosphere. Even now, the Sun is discharging a non-glowing plasma, the solar wind, either toward the planets or into its magnetosphere sheath of double layer Birkeland currents that help shield the solar system from energetic particles coming from interstellar space. The energetic particles are actually captured and directed toward the polar regions of the Sun. The Earth's own magnetosphere similarly shields and directs the solar winds reaching Earth.

The EU group affirms that electric currents in space, called Birkeland currents, provide the circuitry that powers the universe. The Sun, and any other stars, receive their energy from the center of its galaxy, using these unseen circuits. The Sun establishes its own circuits between the planets and the magnetosheath that surrounds the solar system. The stars are not powered by internal thermonuclear explosions, but by these currents, received by their polar regions and then emitted as solar winds. All the complexities of galaxy formation, star nebulas, neutron stars and star evolution can be explained in terms of electromagnetic phenomena, and not by ad hoc theories (as they are called by the EU) that use gravity.

## B. DILEMMA OF CHARGE SEPARATION IN SPACE

The dilemma of the EU group is that they meet the stonewall of paradigms used by the currently accepted dogma and its supporting astrophysicists. Astrophysicists make a simple mathematical calculation to show how much energy it would take to separate all the electrons from the atoms of a teaspoon of salt. *"The stupendous sum of energy was greater than anything they could imagine to be available in a gravity-driven universe. Their conclusion is unavoidable: You can't get charge separation in space. But the question arbitrarily assumes the visible universe is a closed system that 'began' with neutral matter. Such is the power of theoretical assumptions in the absence of experiment and observation. Direct observation will pose the question properly: How could a weak force – gravity – generate a universe observed to be swarming with separated ions and electrons? Answer: Gravity cannot be the elementary force behind the structure and movement of the universe. There is not enough gravitating mass in the visible universe to produce the observed effects of charge separation."*

*"Following the long-accepted view, however, space scientists start with neutral matter. Then they seek to explain how neutral matter becomes ionized and magnetic fields arise. Their models grow increasingly bizarre as space age discoveries reveal complex magnetic fields in unexpected places."* (p. 31, *The Electric Universe*)

In trying to explain the observable universe with gravity, space scientists developed neutron stars, black holes, the Big Bang, dark matter and dark energy. If charge separation in space is properly recognized, then all these crazy concoctions go away. The detection of strong magnetic fields, in space and on the Sun, can only be explained by double-layer currents and charge separation. The EU has an uphill battle, but more information keeps gathering every day from NASA findings to corroborate the truth that the Electric Universe does exist.

## C. CURRENTS BETWEEN CELESTIAL BODIES

The proof of currents between celestial bodies is given by planetary auroras that are directly correlated with coronal and sunspot activity on the Sun. Also, satellites above the Earth's pole detected electrons streaming between the Earth and Sun. Space probes to Jupiter have also detected this same phenomenon. Space probes to comets have revealed that these bodies are dry and have no volatiles, such as water, that can evaporate and create a tail. The tails are created by the increasing density of solar winds as the comet approaches the Sun. The charged particles interact with the comet's atoms and sputter material above its surface, to be carried away in two tails, one of lighter and charged ions and one of heavier dust particles.

But, the real compelling evidence of the interaction of humongous thunderbolts between celestial bodies comes from Mars and the satellites of the outer planets. In particular, Valles Marineris, a deep canyon over 3000 miles long on the face of Mars, can only be the result of sputtering and ejection of materials from an interplanetary plasma discharge. Laser or arc welding and cutting makes a similar mining in commercial metals. Many more features on Mars were characterized by Wal Thornhill (see his publication, "Lightning Scarred Mars and Venus" from the EU Workshop[58]) as being caused by high energy discharges. Only a passing close encounter could have caused this spectacular 3000-mile long gouging of Mars' surface. The electrical scarring is also evidenced by dendritic side canyons and no river delta, as should be revealed by a river system. Mars has a weaker magnetic field than Earth and is less influenced by solar winds that keep Earth more charged. Hence, instead of any arcing focusing on the very weak polar regions of Mars as it did for the stronger magnetic dipole of Earth, it simply moved across the area of closest approach and removed material for a straight length, equivalent to that of the United States, and a width greater than the Grand Canyon. Some the larger ejected pieces of material that reached escape velocity may have become the asteroid-looking satellites of Mars.

The scarring of Venus's surface is postulated, by the author of this paper, to be strong Birkeland currents received directly from the Sun as Venus unluckily moved between the Sun and the closest approach of the brown dwarf star. The two stars were trying to equalize electrical charge and Venus entered the path of their interaction. For the satellites of the outer gas planets, electrical discharges were most likely intercepted by these bodies as they passed between close conjunctions of the passing brown dwarf star or one of its planets and the Sun's planets of either Jupiter or Saturn. Even now, smaller electrical discharges in the glow mode are occurring on the Moon – probably coming from both the Sun's solar winds and passing through the Earth's magnetosphere. Jupiter's moon, Io, is discharging electric arcs, thought originally to be volcanoes of sulfur. Io's discharging is recently known to be related to the aurora storms on Jupiter's polar regions.

Figure 25. Mars Mapping Depicts Valles Marineris and
Olympus Mons Region – Indications of Interplanetary Arc Strikes

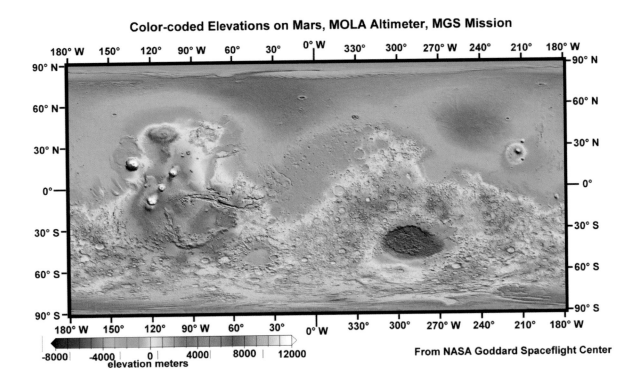

**Color-coded Elevations on Mars, MOLA Altimeter, MGS Mission**

From NASA Goddard Spaceflight Center

Figure 26. Dendritic Structure on Valles Marineris Walls Demonstrates
the Cause is a Large High Energy Plasma Discharge; No Water Erosion
is Responsible for Largest Canyon in the Solar System

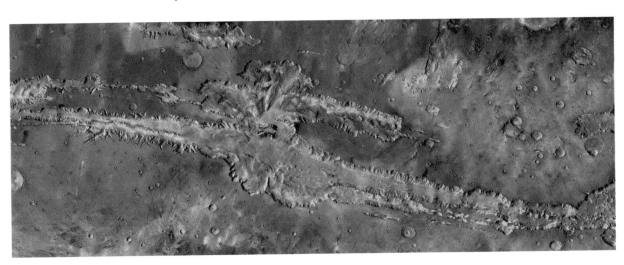

Figure 27. Olympus Mons of Mars is Another Example of an Arc Strike that Can Be Duplicated in a Plasma Laboratory; Reputed to be a Volcano, this Largest Mountain in the Solar System Lacks Many Features that a Typical Volcano Should Have

## D. MAINTAINING THE STABILITY OF ORBITS

An important question should immediately arise. How do all these random events occur in the solar system with the passing of one rogue, alien celestial body? All these events cannot be caused by one crossing or passing. These events require some periodic and repeated passing of one or more celestial bodies, such as an orbiting brown dwarf star system that has not yet been discovered.

Another question also needs to be addressed. How can stability of both star systems be maintained over millions of years? Another EU hypothesis is that forces of electromagnetic processes maintain the roughly rounded and well-spaced orbits of the planets through equalizing their charges. Computerized programs using only gravity indicate that the planets quickly become perturbed by repeated conjunctions with their orbits being thrown into more elliptical and crossing paths. The only other forces available to keep this clockwork of orbiting planets and satellites stable are electromagnetic forces. Electromagnetic forces are about 39 million times stronger than that of gravity, based on an atomic scale. Two objects, one meter apart which both have a mass of one kilogram and a charge of one coulomb, will develop an electric force that is more than $1 \times 10^{20}$ times greater than the gravity force. Therefore, any celestial objects in space will develop the same type of force difference, with the advantage of electric forces being either attractive or repulsive. And, therein lies the reason why celestial bodies can regulate their distances between each other. A system of large celestial bodies would quickly be perturbed into wild orbits if gravity forces, only being attractive, controlled their movements. This outcome using only gravity can be proven by computerized programs that iterate orbits for thousands and millions of years. But, of course, astrophysicists cannot yet comprehend charge separation and charge differences on a celestial scale. Their paradigm about the insistence of parity of charge and the impossibility of charge separation on the scale of celestial objects still rules scientific thought.

## E. INDUCED MAGNETIC FIELDS AND PLANETARY DIPOLES

Another important hypothesis of the EU is that magnetic fields become induced in space surrounding Birkeland currents, which agrees with the theories of James Clerk Maxwell. As stars are formed from *pinch points* created by the magnetic fields along these galactic currents, positive ions of various atoms are formed to make stars become positively-charged anodes. These anodes release electrons through their charged winds toward the planets. The planets become negatively-charged cathodes after receiving electrons from their star. The stars and planets themselves become dipole magnets, since their collected charge is spinning. The dynamics of the combinations of electric and magnetic fields within a star becomes very complex. So, not only will celestial bodies be attracted or repulsed by their respective type and amount of charge, but magnetic forces will also come into play. Because these celestial bodies are spinning, they act like dipole magnets which then have a particular aversion to collecting charged interplanetary particles at their polar regions.

Hence, if one celestial body randomly passes close to another body the combination of not only gravity forces will interact, but the much stronger magnetic and electric forces will overwhelm gravity forces and dominate the outcome. The stronger dipole magnet, presumably the one with greater mass, will be capable of tilting the axis of the other. Or, in the case of Earth, only its mantle and crust were tilted about the planet's core, before resuming its normal vector spin direction by aligning, once again, with the core's spin vector.

## F. THE STRANGE SATURN POLAR CONFIGURATION

Difficulty arises with the EU's hypothesis of the Saturn polar configuration[59] which is not accepted by this paper. This concept is based on a strong belief that the Cosmic Wheel archetype found throughout archeology sites around the world is based on ancient peoples graphically representing what was seen in the skies of earlier times. This archetype is thought to be the linear alignment of Saturn, the arcing Venus, then Mars and finally Earth. These planets orbited Saturn in this alignment inside a glowing protective plasma. Various crescent configurations or reflections on Saturn represented its phases, as light from the Sun reflected off its dense corona sheath. Of course, no such polar alignment has ever been found within or outside the solar system. No amount of physical laws can explain its formation. Its belief is sternly believed to have occurred, based on David Talbott's comparative mythology analyses.

Even more unbelievable is EU's postulation that the break-up of this configuration occurred in mankind's memory where these planets travel to their present orbits around the Sun. Earth's trek from Saturn's orbit of 9 astronomical units to its present orbit of 1 AU would take 10s or perhaps more than 100 years while lacking adequate heat and light from either the Sun or Saturn. EU scientists believe the trek is possible due to the Earth's heat reservoir of its crust, oceans and atmosphere, prior to leaving the light and heat source of Saturn. Anyway, this author discounts this complete storyline for scientific reasons; and, it certainly does not help explain any part of the Great Deluge event. For the EU group, this transition is the end of the ancient Golden Age for humans and the beginning of harsher times when Earth finds a less friendly orbit where night/day, seasonal and climatic cycles begin. My judgement leads me to believe the EU group is stuck on their very own paradigm in the same way that consensus science is stuck on their paradigms.

## G. THE ARCHETYPE MEANINGS

However, with that said, I will not discount their other hypotheses that do directly support this paper's hypothesis for the Great Deluge event. Also, this author does not discount the comparative mythology study by David Talbott. His interpretation of past alien skies, as revealed by his archetypes, is direct proof for the Great Deluge event, except for the Cosmic Wheel and its supposed relation to the Saturn polar configuration. The Cosmic Wheel for this paper is the direct consequence of the presence of the brown dwarf star and its conjunction with Mars, possibly Jupiter, and Earth during one or more crossings of the inner solar system. Of course, the crossing of the brown dwarf star 11,500 years BP is the very possible conjunction of the brown dwarf star, its rogue planet making the close encounter, and Earth. Another related and important archetype for this event is the Great Mountain or Cosmic Wheel with a tongue. The tongue reaches down to Earth and is obviously the plasma discharge arcing between this rogue planet making a close encounter above the Earth's north polar region. More discussions of Talbott's amazing archetypes and his alien skies can be found in his article, "Symbols of an Alien Sky".

## H. IMPORTANCE OF THE ELECTRIC UNIVERSE CONCEPTS

I now must impress upon the reader how important it is to adopt the concepts of the Electric Universe and begin rejecting many of the accepted dogmas of current astrophysicists. You, the reader, if not already exposed to the EU, must transform many of your ideas regarding the physical world, as I did. The true interplay of gravity and electromagnetism is not what was taught, and is still not being taught, by conventional science. Your conversion is important for accepting the facts about the Great Deluge event.

The evolution of the Electric Universe involves many important scientists, some being obscure, through the past 100 or more years. They are: Benjamin Franklin, Michael Faraday, Robert Millikan, Nicklas Tesla, Kristian Birkeland (originator of separate currents in space), Hannes Alfven, Irving Langmuir, Halton Arp, Ralph Juergens, Anthony Peratt and Wallace Thornhill. Please google these scientists and their contributions, which are the foundation of EU concepts. Before leaving this topic, one of the EU scientists, Donald E. Scott, in his book, *The Electric Sky, A Challenge of the Myths of Modern Astronomy*, is quoted.

*"Plasma phenomena are scalable. Their electrical and physical properties remain the same, independent of the size of the plasma. In a laboratory plasma, of course, things happen much more quickly than on, say galaxy scales, but the phenomena are identical – they obey the same laws of physics.*

*"In other words, we make accurate models of cosmic scale plasma behavior in the lab, and generate effects that mimic those observed in space. It has been demonstrated that plasma phenomena can be scaled to fourteen orders of magnitude.*

*"Electric currents flowing in plasmas produce most of the observed astronomical phenomena that remain inexplicable if we assume gravity and magnetism to be the only forces at work."*

# XIII.
# COMPARATIVE STUDY OF THE GREAT DELUGE HYPOTHESES

Different ideas, other than this paper's hypothesis, have been presented about the Great Deluge event. Before moving on, these ideas will be summarized and presented in table form. Upon examination, one will note that this author has combined the most important features of each of the other authors into his own hypothesis, explaining those features of each author that are not or cannot be accepted. Of course, some features are my own including the borrowing of ideas from Zecharia Sitchin's translation of the "Epic Tale of Creation by the Sumerians". This author has added more detail and scientific explanations to Sitchin's translation.

I do not blindly accept the storyline verbatim from any ancient myth, epics or the Bible. Any storyline or pieces of a story that are used shall make sense within the real physical and scientific arenas. To accept all the parts of a story on faith that is handed down, either verbally or in written word, through hundreds and thousands of years is a mistake. Applying these stories as guidance is very useful, but critical judgement and modern science must prevail.

You are also invited to read another Ettinger Journal, "Difficult Issues That Question the Polar Configuration Described in the Saturn Myth", which attempts to eliminate any thoughts that this aligned configuration of Saturn, Venus, Mars and Earth ever existed. I believe this accepted tradition by the EU group is a major stumbling block for their other ideas receiving the credibility they deserve.

Many controversial topics have already been covered. Before you make any judgement as to whether any or one of these hypotheses is closer to the truth or a better objective analysis, read on. Real documentation of witness accounts will be presented to close the case for this world catastrophe of relatively recent times.

The following websites are useful for understanding where the other presented ideas come from and who supports them. Please visit these websites to obtain other important points of view. Be prepared for a very large spectrum of knowledge.

1. www.nasa.gov

2. www.ettingerjournals.com, authored by Douglas Ettinger

3. www.electricuniverse.info

4. www.thunderbolts.info (Thunderbolts Project website for the EU group)

5. www.holoscience.com, authored by Wallace Thornhill

6. www.creationscience.com, authored by Walt Brown

7. *Cataclysm!: Compelling Evidence of a Cosmic Catastrophe in 9500 B.C.*, authored by Allan and Delair

8. www.sitchin.com (official website for Zecharia Sitchin)

9. www.xfacts.com (explains Planet X or the Nemesis star)

10. www.thegreatcourses.com (offers digitized college courses)

Figure 28. Table of Great Deluge Hypotheses and Ideas from 1980 Onward

Sheet 1

| Authors | Underpinning | Direct Cause | Origin of Flood Waters and Rain |
|---|---|---|---|
| NASA and accepted dogma of academia. | Younger Dryas is studied and analyzed; ice cores, sea sediments, tree rings and various dating methods are utilized. | Possible cometary impact; no one idea is promoted, although the Holocene extinction event is recognized. | No global flooding is considered; possibly local floods of rivers or seas occurred at this time. |
| D.S. Allan and J.B. Delair, 1995; *Cataclysm! - Compelling Evidence of a Cosmic Catastrophe in 9500 B.C.* | Phaeton and Atlantis stories told by classical Greeks and the ancient Akkadian story of a destroyed planet, Tiamat. | Gravitational, electrical, and magnetic effects of a close encounter that brought bombarding planetary debris and more water. | Axis tilt and geoid change caused heaped-up seas due to elevation changes, tsunamis of impacts, and added water from planetary debris; melting of ice sheets is not involved because North American Ice Sheet did not exist according to Allan and Delair's hypothesis. |
| Walt Brown, Ph.D., 1980; *In the Beginning - Compelling Evidence for Creation and the Flood.* | Scripture quotations and stories from New American Standard Bible of which the Creation and Noah stories are utilized. | Continuing tidal heating of subterranean super-critical water that is eventually released when hydroplates are stretched apart due to high pressures. No celestial intruder is considered. | Global subterranean chambers with trapped water and minerals that came from the Deep; this water was jettisoned high above the atmosphere and then fell as hail, sleet and muck. |

Sheet 2

| Authors | Spin Axis Change or Crustal/Mantle Shifts | Dating and Span of Period | Aftermath |
|---|---|---|---|
| NASA and accepted dogma of academia. | None occurred. The accepted hypothesis, currently, is that Earth's tilted axis was caused by a rogue planet that struck Earth to create the Moon. | 12,900 to 11,500 years BP; some recovery took as long as 8500 BP based on radiocarbon dating and ocean sediment studies. | Holocene extinction event and general beginning of climatic warming; rise of civilization in the Levant region followed. |
| D.S. Allan and J.B. Delair, 1995; *Cataclysm! – Compelling Evidence of a Cosmic Catastrophe in 9500 B.C.* | Tilt was altered including crustal shifting on top of the Moho layer. Upheaval of seas and mountain ranges resulted. Also, the Earth's rotation was slowed. | A very definitive 11,500 years BP; based on global findings of simultaneous calamities; radiocarbon dating is applied but not completely trusted. | Megafauna extinction and mankind driven back to Stone Ages; collapsed sky or polluted atmosphere from volcanoes and cometary impacts; droughts, hurricanes and lingering subsidence of floodwaters. |
| Walt Brown, Ph.D., 1980, *In the Beginning – Compelling Evidence for Creation and the Flood* | The Earth "rolled" or axis tilted about 30 degrees due to crustal changes and due to accelerated continental drift. | 5000 years BP attempting to match with Biblical scriptures; radiocarbon dating is not trusted beyond 3500 years. | Extinction event occurred; mid-Atlantic ridge with rapid continental drift took place; major mountains ranges formed; comets launched from Earth; and, subterranean hydroplates collapsed. |

Sheet 3

| Authors | Underpinning | Direct Cause | Origin of Flood Waters and Rain |
|---|---|---|---|
| **Wallace Thornhill and David Talbott**, 2016, "Remembering the End of the World" by Talbott and the Thunderbolts Project; and 2005, *Thunderbolts of the Gods* | The Saturn Myth when the planet Saturn reigned as God in a Golden Age of bounty without labor and no seasons or nights; based on corroboration of some important studies of worldwide comparative mythologies. | Disruption of mankind's Golden Age occurred when Earth was perturbed and left Saturn's protective plasma sheath; Earth very soon settled into an orbit around the Sun. Saturn converted from a charged anode-like brown dwarf star to a cathode-like, oppositely charged planet. | No global flooding is considered; however, general global calamitous events happened during the transition from the Golden Age. Ice sheets, cold/dry climates, night and day, and violent weather befell Earth's inhabitants from that time to the present. |
| **Doug Ettinger** of www.ettingerournals.com; 2016, "Great Deluge; Fact or Fiction?", and 2014, "A Brief History of Mankind's Chaotic Past" | Translation of the "Epic Tale of Creation by the Sumerians" as translated by Zecharia Sitchin. Existing advanced civilizations knew of the pending disaster created by Antarctica's ice sheet sliding into the ocean and prepared some of the population. Advanced civilizations existed during antediluvian times and were destroyed. Cradles of civilizations arose again, but with the loss of memory of their previous technical achievements. | Near encounter of some cosmic body, probably of an orbiting brown dwarf star or one of its own planets. The charge difference between this body and Earth caused massive high energy plasma discharges that struck Earth near the north polar region. | Combination of magnetic and gravitational forces changed Earth's geoid by shifting both crust and mantle together; there resulted the heaping of existing seas and oceans, the rapid melting of northern ice sheets, the sliding of Antarctica's ice sheet into the ocean raising sea level and the release of supercritical water under the hydroplates. |

Sheet 4

| Authors | Spin Axis Change or Crustal/Mantle Shifts | Dating and Span of Period | Aftermath |
|---|---|---|---|
| Wallace Thornhill and David Talbott, 2016, "Remembering the End of the World" by Talbott and the Thunderbolts Project; and 2005, *Thunderbolts of the Gods* | Earth, Mars and Venus revolved about Saturn in a polar alignment within a friendly glowing plasma sheath that was dramatically changed to the present configuration within mankind's history. Earth's and Mars's spin axis orientation as when orbiting Saturn was retained due to gyroscopic stability. | Radiocarbon dating is seriously questioned; collapse of previous polar alignment is thought to occur about 5000 years BP and the calamities of ancient Egypt during the Exodus story occurred about 3500 years BP. Dating of ancient languages and civilizations gives guidance to this early dating which deviates completely from more accepted scientific methods. | No specified source of floodwaters is considered; however, general, unspecific global, calamitous events happened during the transition from the Golden Age. Obviously, the trip from Saturn's orbit to Earth's present orbit was precarious for Earth's spaceship riders. Perhaps enough heat retention by the crust, oceans and atmosphere allowed survival. |
| Doug Ettinger of ww.ettinger journals.com; 2016, "Great Deluge; Fact or Fiction?", and 2014, "A Brief History of Mankind's Chaotic Past" | The axis did change for the crust and mantle, but not for Earth's core; the crust and mantle were magnetized and yanked about 25 to 30 degrees of latitude, with respect to the core, by the magnetic forces of a close encounter of another magnetic celestial body. The mantle then resumed the same rotation vector as the core. | Most catastrophic events occurred together in a short period of time centered around 11,500 years BP; due to incorrect application of the $^{14}C/^{12}C$ ratio radiocarbon dating of Younger Dryas spanning 1400 years is wrong; the event occurred over weeks or months with recovery over hundreds of years. | A major extinction event occurred; peak sea level dropped slowly while re-freezing of polar ice caps took place; volcanism and earthquakes along with hydroplate releases caused collapsed skies that persisted for hundreds of years; some fast folding and upheaval of mountain ranges; changes to climate of Siberian grasslands to tundra having $H_2O$ and $CO_2$ locked in the permafrost. |

# XIV.
# COMPELLING EVIDENCE
# USING WITNESS ACCOUNTS

The previous sections of this paper provide technical and physical reasons for why the Great Deluge can happen and did happen. Once you realize that such an event can actually occur you are then prepared to move away from the mythical and fantasy-like ideas imprinted on your mind. Traditions and sagas being told and recorded by many ancient cultures throughout the world suddenly become real. The arrival of a global flood is no longer unbelievable; it can really happen scientifically and, now without question, it certainly did.

## A. VERBAL AND WRITTEN TRANSFER OF WITNESS ACCOUNTS THROUGH HUNDREDS OF GENERATIONS

The famous linguist Charles Berlitz reports that early Jesuit missionaries in China located a 4,320-volume work "compiled by Imperial Edict and containing 'all knowledge'. It states, *"The Earth was shaken to its foundations. The sky sank lower toward the north. The sun, moon, and stars changed their motions. The Earth fell to pieces and the waters in its bosom rushed upward with violence and overflowed the Earth. Man had rebelled against the high gods and the system of the Universe was in disorder."* (p. 129, Brown) Literally, from the perspective of Chinese observers, when the crust/mantle shifted and moved northward in China, either the sky should have been lifted instead of sinking or the horizon should have sunk. Perhaps the true meaning was lost in the translation. Nevertheless, the frame of reference of the sky with respect to an observer on Earth changed dramatically enough to be recorded along with its accompanying disasters.

According to Velikovsky, Hebrew tradition stated that, "the Sun did not proceed on its course during the Day of Passage." Of course, the Hebrew Old Testament does account for Noah's flood and the 40 days and nights of continuous rain which was given to them by the Babylonians when the Hebrews were exiled. The Genesis and Noah stories are really abridged accounts of these same stories handed down by the Sumerians who flourished about 4000 B.C. The Sumerian story is given in the "Epic Tale of Creation" which was translated by Zecharia Sitchin. His translation revealed a much more detailed account of the

Flood, which is told to be a combination of a celestial disturbance and the movement of Antarctica's ice sheets into the ocean. These translations were taken from Babylonian cylinder seals made from hardstones and clay tablets having engravings of Mesopotamian cuneiform. The cylinder seals were linked to Sumerian clay tablets that were well-preserved in the libraries of buried Mesopotamian cities. The Sumerian writers of these times claimed that stories of the Flood were handed down from much earlier times; the stories were not the product of their God or Gods.

Allan and Delair's compilation and analysis of myths, legends and traditions is perhaps the best research now available. It covers all geographical and cultural regions of all the continents. One striking observation is their distinction between the primitive and the rising civilized nations after the Deluge. The American Indians maintained very close or similar ideas about past events, whereas the so-called civilized peoples present a more inconsistent and garbled set of ideas. I quote directly from p. 149, Allan and Delair: *"Legend has one great foe to its perpetuation – civilization. Civilization brings with it a contempt for everything which it cannot understand; skepticism becomes the synonym for intelligence; men no longer repeat – they doubt, they dissect, they sneer, they reject, they invent. If the myth survives this treatment, the poets take it up and make it their stock-in-trade – they decorate it in a masquerade of frippery and finery, feathers and furbelows, like a clown dressed for a fancy ball; and the poor barbarian legend survives at last, if it survives at all, like the Conflagration in Ovid, or King Arthur in Tennyson – a hippopotamus smothered in flowers, jewels, and laces _ _ _."*

*"Initial compilers and purveyors of traditions to convey in clear and unambiguous terms often quite elaborate original concepts and sagas to essentially illiterate mass audiences, it was necessary for these traditions to be presented in simplified or general form. The resultant statements were therefore frequently abrupt or terse, and tended to emphasize the more easily comprehended effects rather than technically complex causes _ _ _"*

Many of these legends of catastrophe are divided into a terrible conflagration and global flooding. And within this grouping, most claim the conflagration preceded the flood which then smothered the fires. Such is the proven case with the forensics of buried trees and other flora in northern Siberia. The conflagration events included aerial falls of combustible/resinous materials, mass burning of vegetation, boiling rivers/lakes/oceans, lightning, cyclic winds, thunder and din.

The cause of such calamity was very often attributed to cosmic bodies either passing over and or striking Earth. These bodies brought aerial falls of hail, gravel, stones and dust; aerial falls of ferruginous materials; the break-up of cometary bodies; axial/rotational changes of Earth, poisoned atmosphere and collapsed skies (lingering dust and gases shielding the Sun); and stellar relocations.

For many traditions, landform changes also occurred, such as axial/rotational changes of Earth, uplifting of mountain ranges, sinking or raising of plateaus, lost lands and lakes, and volcanism. These worldwide changes to the crust are linked to the axial changes of the crust-mantle unit shift which quickly changed Earth's geoid.

Allan and Delair's final conclusion after reviewing their global collection of traditions and legends is that — "Only truly independent recollections would contain such superficially contradictory yet geographically correct details" (p. 161, Allan and Delair). Data gathered by these authors of geology/paleontology, botany/zoology, and tradition/legends tells virtually the same story - that the Great Deluge did happen.

Allan and Delair, page 150, make a claim in the introduction to their table for *"Geographical distribution of traditions of the Deluge and Great Catastrophe"* that the survivors were forewarned of the impending disaster. I am not clear how such a statement can be made. The survivors were the lucky ones who resided coincidently in places out of harm's way from thunderbolts and conflagration, and at higher altitudes away from the rising oceans. Of course, a known exception is Noah who was not only warned, but given specific directions about how to survive. This amazing Noah story will be discussed later in greater detail. Interestingly, Allan and Delair include vanished regions: Atlantis in the Atlantic, Gobi Sea in Central Asia, Lemuria in the Indian Ocean, Hyperborea in the Arctic, Mu in the Pacific, and Tritonis in North Africa.

Allan and Delair's table, pages 162 to 165, for *"Traditions specifying particular catastrophic effects. (for the various continental regions)"* are suggested as required reading. As is indicated in these tables, the "conflagration/firestorm" calamity has numerous examples for each major world region, although outnumbered by the traditions of the Deluge event. Another interesting observation is that the various "aerial fall" stories passed down, come from northern Europe and the Americas. No cultures in Siberia had stories to tell because they probably all perished. The "aerial fall" are expected to be witnessed in the northern polar regions and in the Americas because the arc discharge struck Earth in northern Canada and ejected debris circumferentially into Europe, Siberia, Canada, Greenland and Alaska. Other debris that was sputtered from the crust by the arc discharge went in the direction of impact which was a southerly direction centered along the 75° meridian line that goes through the USA and South America. The most aerial fall of hail, gravel, stones, combustible materials and ferruginous substances is expected to fall mostly on North and South America, which it did. Since, the hydroplates were pulled apart mostly in the Arctic, their release of similar aerial fall materials is expected in regions surrounding the Arctic Circle, as is indicated by Allan and Delair's table of catastrophic traditions. The table also corroborates that fewer or no traditions of this type are indicated in Africa, Australia and Oceania. These areas of the world would certainly witness dusty atmospheres and collapsed skies, but would not be in direct line of sight of the proposed trajectory of ejected materials and aerial falls from arc discharges of the Hudson Bay region or the Arctic hydroplate high pressure water releases.

For reader convenience the very important tables for "Traditions specifying particular catastrophic effects" found in *Cataclysm!* by D. S. Allan & J. B. Delair and published by Inner Traditions International and Bear & Company, © 1997, is provided below. Permission for reprinting was graciously granted by the publisher at www.Innertraditions.com.

## Figure 29. Geographical distribution of traditions
## of the Deluge and Great Catastrophe by Allan and Delair

*Table 3A*
**Geographical distribution of traditions of the Deluge and Great Catastrophe**

A selection of the 500 or more known examples, compiled from numerous sources. The survivors of the Flood in all the legends range from a single individual to a small group. All seemed to have been forewarned of the impending disaster. They escaped by seeking high ground, trees, caves or by means of various objects which would float.

## OLD WORLD
### EUROPE
**Britain:** *Druidic*
**Finland:** *Finns*
**Germany**
**Greece:** *Ancient Greeks*
**Iceland:** *Norse sagas*
**Italy:** *Romans*
**Lapland:** *Lapps*
**Lithuania**
**Russa:** *Voguls*
**Savoy**
**Scandinavia:** *Norse traditions*
**Sicily**
**Slavonia:** *Slavs*
**Spain**
**Transylvania**
**Wales:** *Druidic Triads*
**Asia**
**Afghanistan:** *Afghans*
**Andaman Islands**
**Arabia**
**Armenia**
**Assyria**
**Babylonia:** *(Hasisadra or Xisuthrus),*
   *( Ut-Napishtim)*
**Burma:** *Chingpaws, Karens*
**Cambodia & Lagos:** *Bahnars,*
   *Bannavs*
**Chaldea:** *(Hasisadra)*
**China:** *Yunnan: Lolos*

**India:** Assam: *Ahoms, Anais, Lushais,*
   *Singpos;* Bengal: *Hos (Larka Kols),*
   *Kamars, Mumdas (Mundaris), San-*
   *tahs;* Central India: *Bhilos, Kamars;*
   Kashmir: *Kashmiris*
**Indonesia:** Borneo (Kalimantan): *Ot-*
   *Danoms, Dusan, Dyaks;* Ceram:
   *Alfoors;* Sumatra: *Bataks, Engano,*
   *Nias;* Timor: *Roth;* W. Irian:
   *Mamberano*
**Japan**
**Malaysia:** *Benna Jakim, Kelantan*
**Mergui Archipelago:** *Selungs*
**Mongolia**
**Palestine:** *Phoenicians, Hebrews (scriptural*
   *sources: Genesis, Exodus, Job, Josua*
   *& Revelations)*
**Persia**
**Philippines**
**Phrygia (Anatolia)**
**Siberia:** *Buriats, Tatars, Kalmaks*
**Sikkim**
**Sri Lanka:** *Kalyani*
**Sumer**
**Syria**
**Taiwan (Formosa):** *Ami, Bunun and aborig-*
   *inal tribes*
**Tibet:** *Lepcha*
**Turkestan:** *Bokharas, Tatars*

### AFRICA
*Bantu*
*Basutto (probably borrowed)*
*Bermagai*
*Carthaginians*
*Egyptians (several versions)*
*Hottentots*
*Kangas*
*Loangas*
*Massai (probably borrowed)*
*Ovahereros*
*Somalis*
*Sudanese*
*Wanyoros*

### AUSTRALASIA & OCEANIA
**Australia:** Queenslandl: *Aborigines;* Victoria:
   *Kurnai, L. Tyres tribe*
**New Zealand:** *Maori*
**Papua**
**Ociania:** *Micronesia, Melanesia, Polynesia*
**Fiji:** *Fijians*
**Hawaii:** *Hawaiians*
**Hudson Islands:** *Nanumanghan*
**Leeward Islands (incl. Tahiti)**
**Mangaia (Hervey) Islands**
**Marquesas Islands**
**New Hebrides**
**Pelew Islands**
**Samoa**
**Sandwich Islands**
**Society Islands**

## NEW WORLD
### NORTH AMERICA
*Aleuts (Aleutians)*
*Algonguins (incl. Foxes & Sacs)*
*Apaches (Arizona)*
*Arapaho*
*Ashochimi (California)*
*Athabascans (Canada)*
*Bella Coola (Canada)*
*Caddoque*
*Cayus*
*Cegiha*
*Cherokee*
*Chewkee*
*Chickasaws (Dakotas)*
*Chimakums (Washington)*
*Chippewa*
*Chocktaw (Oklahoma)*
*Cree (Canada)*
*Delaware*
*Dogrids (Canada)*
*Eskimo (Canada, Alaska, Greenland)*
*Gros-Ventres (Montana)*
*Haida (NW Pacific Coast)*
*Hareskin Indians (Canada)*
*Hopi (SW states USA)*
*Iroquois (North-east)*
*Kaska (Brit. Columbia)*
*Kathlamet*
*Kato (California)*
*Klamath (Oregon)*
*Kolush (Alaska)*
*Kinsteneax (Missouri)*
*Kootenay*
*Kwakiutls (NW Pacific Coast)*
*Lenni-Lenapes*
*Lilluets*
*Luisenos (California)*

*Loucheux (Dinjieh) (Brit. Columbia)*
*Maidu (California)*
*Maitaquais (Canada)*
*Makah (Washington)*
*Mandan*
*Muskwaki (Canada)*
*Natchez (Mississippi)*
*Nez-Perces*
*Ojidway (Canada)*
*Oraibi*
*Papagos (Arizona)*
*Pawnee*
*Pima (Arizona)*
*Quilentes (Washington)*
*Salishan (Okinagan) (Washington)*
*Shoshona (Colorado-Utah)*
*Slave Indians (Canada)*
*Snolionish (Puget Sound)*
*Snoqualmi (California)*
*South River Indians (California)*
*Southern Ute (California)*
*Taculli (Takahli) (Canada)*
*Tahoe Indians (Nevada)*
*Tchiglit (Tingit) (Alaska)*
*Thompson Indians (Canada)*
*Tinneh (several versions)*
*Tolowa (Oregon)*
*Tsimshian*
*Tuleyome Indians (California)*
*Ute (Colorado)*
*Washo (California)*
*Wichita (Oklahoma)*
*Wintun (California)*
*Wyandot*
*Yana (California)*
*Zuni (New Mexico)*

### CENTRAL AMERICA
**Guatemala:** *Maya*
**Mexico:** *Aztec, Maya, Mixtec, Toltec, Cora,*
   *Huichol, Michoacans, Tarahumare,*
   *Texpis, Zuni*
**Nicaragua**
**Panama:** *Cunas*
**Salvador**
**Caribbean:** *Caribs, Haitians*

### SOUTH AMERICA
**Argentina:** *Araucanians, Tierra del Fuegans*
**Brazil:** *Aberderys, Bororo, Cabo Frio Indians,*
   *Caraga, Cashinaua, Caura, Chincha,*
   *Coroado (kainganag) Indians, Guarani,*
   *Ipuriana, Kataushy Indians, Maypures,*
   *Parray, Timanacs, Tupi*
**Bolivia:** *Yurucares*
**Chile:** *Araucas*
**Colombia:** *Chibcha or Muyscaya, Cuna*
**Equador:** *Carari, Jivaro*
**Peru:** *Chiriguana, Incas (several versions)*
**Paraguay:** *Mbocobi*
**Venezuela:** *Tamanaki*

### VANISHED REGIONS
**Atlantic:** *Atlantis*
**Central Asia:** Gobi Sea
**Indian Ocean:** Lemuria
**Arctic:** Hyperborea
**Pacific:** Mu
**North Africa:** Tritonis

## Figure 30. Traditions Specifying Particular
## Catastrophic Effects by Allan and Delair

*Table 3B*
**Traditions specifying particular catastrophic effects.**
**Europe and Asia**

Column legend (left to right):

1. Aerial falls: hail, gold, gravel, stones, dust
2. Aerial falls: combustible/resinous materials
3. Aerial falls: ferruginous substances
4. Effects on vegetation
5. Axial/rotational changes
6. Boiling rivers/lakes/oceans
7. Break-up and fall of celestial visitor
8. Collapsed sky
9. The coming of ice
10. Conflagration/firestorm
11. Cyclonic winds
12. Deluge/flood
13. Description of celestial visitor
14. Lightning
15. Poisoned atmosphere
16. Prolonged darkness
17. Steam
18. Stellar derangement
19. Thunder/noise/din
20. Topographical changes
21. Records of lost lands and lakes
22. References to pre-Diluvian civilisation

| Tradition | 1 | 2 | 3 | 4 | 5 | 6 | 7 | 8 | 9 | 10 | 11 | 12 | 13 | 14 | 15 | 16 | 17 | 18 | 19 | 20 | 21 | 22 | Region |
|---|---|---|---|---|---|---|---|---|---|---|---|---|---|---|---|---|---|---|---|---|---|---|---|
| BRITAIN: Druids | □ | ■ | □ | □ | □ | □ | □ | ■ | ■ | ■ | □ | □ | ■ | □ | □ | □ | ■ | □ | □ | | | | **EUROPE** |
| RUSSIA: Voguls | □ | □ | □ | □ | ■ | □ | □ | □ | □ | □ | □ | ■ | □ | □ | □ | □ | □ | □ | □ | | | | |
| FINLAND: Finns | ■ | □ | ■ | □ | □ | □ | □ | □ | □ | □ | ■ | □ | □ | □ | □ | □ | □ | □ | □ | | | | |
| Apollodorus | ■ | □ | ■ | □ | □ | □ | ■ | □ | ■ | ■ | □ | ■ | □ | □ | □ | □ | □ | □ | □ | | | | **HELLENIC** authors |
| Hesiod | □ | ■ | □ | □ | □ | □ | □ | □ | ■ | □ | □ | □ | □ | ■ | □ | ■ | ■ | ■ | □ | | | | |
| Plato | □ | □ | □ | □ | ■ | □ | □ | □ | ■ | □ | □ | ■ | □ | □ | □ | ■ | ■ | ■ | ■ | | | | |
| various | □ | □ | □ | □ | □ | □ | ■ | □ | ■ | □ | ■ | □ | □ | □ | □ | □ | □ | □ | □ | | | | |
| ICELAND: Voluspa | □ | □ | □ | □ | □ | □ | □ | ■ | □ | ■ | □ | □ | ■ | □ | □ | □ | ■ | ■ | ■ | | | | |
| IRELAND | □ | □ | □ | □ | □ | □ | ■ | □ | □ | ■ | □ | ■ | □ | □ | □ | □ | □ | □ | □ | | | | |
| ITALY: various authors | □ | □ | □ | ■ | □ | □ | ■ | □ | ■ | □ | ■ | □ | ■ | ■ | ■ | ■ | □ | ■ | ■ | | | | |
| LAPPLAND: Lapps | □ | □ | □ | □ | □ | □ | □ | □ | ■ | □ | □ | □ | □ | □ | □ | □ | □ | □ | □ | | | | |
| LITHUANIA | □ | □ | □ | ■ | □ | □ | □ | ■ | □ | □ | □ | □ | □ | □ | □ | □ | □ | □ | □ | | | | |
| SCANDINAVIA: *Eddas* | ■ | □ | □ | □ | □ | ■ | □ | ■ | □ | ■ | ■ | ■ | □ | ■ | ■ | ■ | ■ | □ | □ | | | | |
| SPAIN | □ | □ | □ | □ | □ | □ | □ | □ | ■ | □ | □ | □ | □ | □ | □ | □ | □ | □ | □ | | | | |
| TRANSYLVANIA | □ | □ | ■ | □ | □ | □ | □ | □ | □ | □ | □ | □ | □ | □ | □ | □ | □ | □ | □ | | | | |
| WALES: *Triads* | □ | □ | □ | □ | □ | □ | □ | □ | ■ | □ | □ | □ | □ | □ | □ | □ | □ | ■ | □ | | | | |
| Coptic | ■ | □ | □ | ■ | □ | □ | □ | □ | □ | □ | □ | □ | □ | □ | □ | □ | □ | □ | □ | | | | **RELIGIOUS SOURCES** |
| Hebrew | ■ | □ | ■ | □ | □ | □ | □ | □ | □ | □ | □ | ■ | □ | □ | □ | □ | □ | □ | □ | | | | |
| Muslim | ■ | □ | □ | □ | □ | □ | □ | □ | □ | □ | □ | □ | □ | □ | □ | □ | □ | □ | □ | | | | |
| AFGHANISTAN: Afghans | □ | □ | □ | □ | □ | □ | □ | ■ | □ | □ | □ | □ | □ | □ | □ | □ | □ | □ | □ | | | | **ASIA** |
| ANDAMAN ISLANDS | □ | □ | □ | □ | □ | □ | ■ | □ | □ | □ | □ | □ | □ | □ | □ | □ | □ | □ | □ | | | | |
| ARABIA | □ | □ | □ | □ | □ | □ | □ | □ | □ | □ | □ | □ | □ | □ | □ | □ | □ | □ | □ | | | | |
| BABYLONIA & ASSYRIA | ■ | □ | □ | □ | □ | ■ | ■ | □ | □ | ■ | □ | □ | □ | □ | □ | □ | □ | □ | □ | | | | |
| BORNEO | □ | □ | □ | □ | ■ | □ | ■ | □ | □ | □ | □ | □ | ■ | □ | □ | □ | □ | □ | □ | | | | |
| BURMA: Chingpaws | □ | □ | □ | □ | □ | □ | □ | □ | □ | □ | □ | □ | □ | □ | □ | □ | □ | □ | □ | | | | |
| CAMBODIA/LAOS | □ | □ | □ | □ | □ | □ | □ | □ | □ | □ | □ | □ | □ | □ | □ | □ | □ | □ | □ | | | | |
| CHINA | □ | □ | □ | □ | ■ | □ | ■ | □ | □ | □ | □ | □ | ■ | □ | □ | □ | □ | □ | □ | | | | |
| TAIWAN: Banum | □ | □ | □ | □ | □ | □ | □ | □ | □ | □ | □ | □ | □ | □ | □ | □ | □ | □ | □ | | | | |
| INDIA: several accounts | □ | □ | □ | □ | □ | □ | ■ | □ | □ | □ | □ | □ | □ | ■ | ■ | ■ | □ | □ | □ | | | | |
| INDONESIA: Dusan | □ | ■ | □ | □ | □ | □ | □ | ■ | □ | □ | □ | □ | □ | □ | □ | □ | □ | □ | □ | | | | |
| CERAM | □ | □ | □ | □ | □ | □ | □ | □ | □ | □ | □ | □ | □ | □ | □ | □ | □ | □ | □ | | | | |
| FLORES | □ | □ | □ | □ | □ | □ | □ | □ | □ | □ | □ | □ | □ | □ | □ | □ | □ | □ | □ | | | | |
| SUMATRA: Bataks | □ | □ | □ | □ | □ | □ | □ | □ | □ | □ | □ | □ | □ | □ | □ | □ | □ | □ | □ | | | | |
| TIMOR | □ | □ | □ | □ | □ | □ | □ | □ | □ | □ | □ | □ | □ | □ | □ | □ | □ | □ | □ | | | | |
| W. IRIAN | □ | □ | □ | □ | □ | □ | □ | □ | □ | □ | □ | ■ | □ | □ | □ | □ | □ | □ | □ | | | | |
| JAPAN | □ | □ | □ | □ | □ | □ | □ | □ | □ | □ | □ | □ | ■ | □ | □ | □ | □ | □ | □ | | | | |
| MALAYSIA | □ | □ | □ | □ | □ | □ | □ | □ | □ | □ | □ | □ | □ | □ | □ | □ | □ | □ | □ | | | | |
| MERGUI ARCH: Selungs | □ | □ | □ | □ | □ | □ | □ | □ | □ | □ | □ | □ | □ | □ | □ | ■ | ■ | ■ | □ | | | | |
| MONGOLIA | □ | □ | □ | □ | □ | □ | □ | □ | □ | □ | □ | □ | □ | □ | □ | ■ | □ | □ | □ | | | | |
| PALESTINE: Jews | ■ | □ | □ | □ | □ | □ | □ | □ | □ | □ | □ | □ | □ | □ | □ | □ | □ | □ | □ | | | | |
| PERSIA | □ | □ | ■ | □ | □ | ■ | ■ | ■ | ■ | ■ | □ | □ | ■ | □ | □ | □ | □ | □ | □ | | | | |
| PHILIPPINES | □ | □ | □ | □ | □ | □ | □ | □ | □ | □ | □ | □ | □ | □ | □ | □ | □ | □ | □ | | | | |
| SIBERIA: Buriats | □ | □ | □ | □ | □ | □ | □ | □ | □ | □ | □ | □ | □ | □ | □ | □ | □ | □ | □ | | | | |
| SIKKIM | □ | □ | □ | □ | □ | □ | □ | □ | □ | □ | □ | □ | □ | □ | □ | □ | □ | □ | □ | | | | |
| SRI LANKA: Kalyani | □ | □ | □ | □ | □ | □ | □ | □ | □ | □ | □ | □ | □ | □ | □ | □ | □ | ■ | ■ | | | | |
| SUMER | □ | □ | □ | □ | □ | □ | □ | □ | □ | ■ | □ | □ | □ | □ | □ | □ | □ | □ | □ | | | | |
| TIBET: Lepcha | □ | □ | □ | □ | □ | ■ | □ | □ | □ | □ | □ | □ | □ | □ | □ | □ | ■ | □ | □ | | | | |

*Table 3B (Continued)*

## Traditions specifying particular catastrophic effects.
## The Americas

Column key (read diagonally, left to right):

1. Aerial falls: hail, gold, gravel, stones, dust
2. Aerial falls: combustible/resinous materials
3. Aerial falls: ferruginous substances
4. Effects on vegetation
5. Axial/rotational changes
6. Boiling rivers/lakes/oceans
7. Break-up and fall of celestial visitor
8. Collapsed sky
9. The coming of ice
10. Conflagration/firestorm
11. Cyclonic winds
12. Deluge/flood
13. Description of celestial visitor
14. Lightning
15. Poisoned atmosphere
16. Prolonged darkness
17. Steam
18. Stellar derangement
19. Thunder/noise/din
20. Topographical changes
21. Records of lost lands and lakes
22. References to pre-Diluvian civilisation

|  |  |
|---|---|
| ALASKA: Kolushes | NORTH AMERICA |
| Tlinkits | |
| ALEUTIAN Is | |
| ARIZONA: Papagos | |
| Pawnees | |
| Pimas | |
| BR COLUMBIA: Kaska | |
| Loucheux | |
| Okanagan | |
| CALIFORNIA: Katos | |
| Southern Utes | |
| Wintun | |
| COLORADO: Utes | |
| DAKOTAS: Chickasaws | |
| Delaware Indians | |
| GREENLAND: Eskimos | |
| NEVADA: Tahoe Indians | |
| NEW MEXICO: Zunis | |
| N.W. PACIFIC COAST: Haida | |
| OKLAHOMA: Chocktaws | |
| S.W. STATES: Hopi | |
| WASHINGTON: Chimakums | |
| Chippewas | |
| Makahs | |
| Mandans | |
| Quilentes | |
| MEXICO/: Aztec | MESO-AMERICA |
| GUATEMALA: Maya | |
| Mixtec | |
| CARIBBEAN: Caribs | |
| NICARAGUA | |
| ARGENTINA: Araucanians | SOUTH AMERICA |
| BRAZIL: Aberdervs | |
| Botocudos | |
| Cashinaua | |
| Coroado | |
| Ipurianas | |
| Kataushi | |
| Parrays | |
| Tupis/Guaranis | |
| BOLIVIA: Yurucares | |
| COLOMBIA: Chibchas | |
| EQUADOR: Cararis | |
| GUIANAS: Caribs | |
| Macusis | |
| PANAMA: Cunas | |
| PARAGUAY: Mbocobi | |
| PERU: several accounts | |
| VENEZUELA | |

*Table 3B (Continued)*

## Traditions specifying particular catastrophic effects.
## Australasia, Oceania and Africa

Column headings (read diagonally, left to right):

1. Aerial falls: hail, gold, gravel, stones, dust
2. Aerial falls: combustible/resinous materials
3. Aerial falls: ferruginous substances
4. Effects on vegetation
5. Axial/rotational changes
6. Boiling rivers/lakes/oceans
7. Break-up and fall of celestial visitor
8. Collapsed sky
9. The coming of ice
10. Conflagration/firestorm
11. Cyclonic winds
12. Deluge/flood
13. Description of celestial visitor
14. Lightning
15. Poisoned atmosphere
16. Prolonged darkness
17. Steam
18. Stellar derangement
19. Thunder/noise/din
20. Topographical changes
21. Records of lost lands and lakes
22. References to pre-Diluvian civilisation

**AUSTRALASIA & OCEANIA**

| Tradition | Catastrophic effects (see column list 1–22) |
|---|---|
| AUSTRALIA: Aborigines | conflagration; deluge |
| Kurnia | conflagration |
| Lake Tyers Tribe | conflagration |
| FIJI | boiling rivers; deluge; stellar derangement; thunder |
| HAWAII | deluge |
| LEEWARD Is: Tahitians | conflagration; deluge |
| NEW ZEALAND: Maoris | aerial falls (combustible); conflagration; deluge; thunder |
| PAPUA | deluge |
| SAMOA | aerial falls (combustible); boiling rivers; conflagration; deluge |
| POLYNESIA: general | deluge |

**AFRICA**

| Tradition | Catastrophic effects (see column list 1–22) |
|---|---|
| Bantus | prolonged darkness |
| Bermagai | conflagration |
| Egyptians | conflagration |
| Hottentots | conflagration |
| Kangas | — |
| Loangas | conflagration |
| Masai & Basutos | deluge; topographical changes |
| Ovahereros | conflagration |
| Somalis | — |
| Sudanese | deluge; thunder; topographical changes |
| Wanyoros | vegetation |

## REFERENCES

1. Donnelly, I. 1894. *Ragnarok: The Age of Fire and Gravel* (New York), vi + 452pp; p117.

2. Donnelly, I. 1894. *Ibid.*

3. Kalisch, M M. 1858. *A Historical and Critical Commentary on the Old Testament: Genesis* (London), viii + 780pp; p205.

4. Miller, F J (transl). 1916. Ovid, P. *Metamorphoses* (London & New York); see Book 11, fable 1.

5. Frazer, J G (transl). 1921. Apollodorus *Mythulogica*, 2 vols (London).

6. Babbitt, F C. 1936. Plutarch *Isis and Osiris*, 5 vols, (London & Harvard Univ Press); vol 5, pp41,49.

7. Rackham, H (transl). 1938. Pliny the Elder *Natural History*, 10 vols, (London); vol ii, p91.

8. Jones, H L (transl). 1924. Strabo *The Geography*, 8 vols, (London); vol vii, 3, 8.

9. Gregory, J W. 1896. *The Great Rift Valley* (London), xxi + 422pp; p325.

10. Darmesteter, J (transl). 1883. *Zend-Avesta: The Vendidad*, 3 vols, (Oxford); pt 11, p95.

11. Darmesteter, J (transl). 1883. *Op cit*; p95.

12. Gray, L H (ed). 1917. A J Carnoy in *The Mythology of All Races*, 13 vols, (Boston); vol vi, pp268ff.

13. Cumont, F. 1931. "La Fin du monde selon les mages occidentaux", *Rev de l'histoire des religions*, p41.

14. Teit, J A. 1917. "Kaska Tales", *J Am Folk*, vol xxx, p440.

15. Alexander, H B. 1916. *North American Mythology* (New York), xxiv + 325pp; p25.

16. Eusebius, P. 1913. *Werke* (Leipzig), tr by R.Helm, 8 vols; vol v, "Die Chronik".
Frazer, J G. 1918. *Folklore in the Old Testament* (London), 3 vols; vol 1, p159.

17. Way, A. 1924. *The Riddle of the Earth* (London), 251pp; chap xi, pp160–161.

18. *Book of Revelation*. Chap 6, v12–16; Chap 7, v2; Chap 8, v5, 7–12; Chap 9, v1–13, 17–19; Chap 10, v6; Chapt 12, v7–9, 15–16.
19. Kellett, E E. 1927. *The Story of Myths* (London), 275pp; p27.
20. Gadd, C J. *The Babylonian Story of the Deluge and the Epic of Gilgamesh* (Brit Mus, London), 57pp.
21. Suryakanta, S. 1950. *The Flood Legend in Sanskrit Literature*, 4 vols (Delhi).
22. Miller, F J (transl). 1916. *Ibid.*
23. Miller, F J (transl). 1916. *Ibid.*
24. Chi, T. 1946. *A Short History of Chinese Civilisation* (London), 335pp; pp14–15.
25. Dorsey, G A. 1906. *Pawnee Mythology* (Washington), 546pp; pt 1, p35.
26. Olrik, A. 1922. *Ragnarok* (Cologne), German edn, xvi + 484pp; p407.
27. Miller, F J (transl). 1916. *Loc cit.*
28. Miller, F J (transl). 1916. *Ibid.*
29. Anderson, R B. 1888. *Norse Mythology* (Chicago), 473pp; p416.
30. Donnelly, I. 1895. *Op cit*; see p141.
31. Miller, F J (transl). 1916. *Ibid.*
32. Miller, F J (transl). 1916. *Ibid.*
33. Powell, J W. 1879. *Pop Sci Mon.*
    Powell, J W. 1881. "Sketch of the Mythology of the North American Indians", *Rep Bur Am Ethnol*, Washington, 1st report 1879–1880; pp17–56.
34. Rawlinson, H (transl). 1889. Herodotus *Historia*, 4 vols, (London); vol iii, p5.
35. Jones, H L (transl). 1924. *Op cit*; see vol vii, 3, 8.
36. Apollonius Rhodius. 1912. *Argonautica* (London), 454pp; book ii.
37. *Koran*. Sura 89, v.5 etc.
    Lenormant, F. 1869. *Manual d'Histoire Ancienne de l'Orient*, 3 vols, (Paris); vol iii, p295.
38. Maurice, T. 1799. *The Ancient History of Hindustan*, 2 vols, (London); vol 1, p304.
39. Williamson, R W. 1933. *Religious and Cosmic Beliefs of Central Polynesia*, 2 vols, (Cambridge); see vol i, p8.
40. Ellis, W. 1829. *Polynesian Researches*, 2 vols, (London); vol ii, pp57f.
41. Le Plongeon, A. 1896. *Queen Moô and the Egyptian Sphinx* (London), lxv + 277pp.
42. Spence, J L. 1933. *The Problem of Lemuria, the sunken continent of the Pacific* (London), 249pp; p54.
43. Bancroft, H H. 1875–6. *The Native Races of the Pacific States of North America*, 5 vols, (London); see vol 4, p306.
44. Bury, R G (transl). 1929. Plato *Timaeus* (Loeb Classical Library, New York), vol 7, 24E, 25 B-D.
45. Babcock, W H. 1922. *Legendary Islands of the Atlantic* (New York), 196pp.
46. Spence, H R. 1866. *Legends and Theories of the Buddhists* (London & Edinburgh), lvi + 244pp; p6.
47. Bellamy, H S. 1949. *Moons, Myths and Man* (London), 312pp; p108.
48. Gray, L H (ed). 1916 in H B Alexander (ed) in *The Mythology of All Races*, 13 vols, (Boston); vol x, p222.
49. Lockett, H G. 1933. "Unwritten Literature of the Hopi", *Univ Okla Soc Sci Bull*, no:2, May 15th, pp69–70.
50. McDowell, B, & J E Fletcher. 1962. "Avalanche: 3500 Peruvians Perish in Seven Minutes", *Natn Geogr Mag*, June 1962, p871.
51. Bellamy, H S. 1949. *Op cit*, p80.
52. Cushing, F H. 1896. "Outlines of Zuni Creation Myths", *Rep Bur Am Ethnol*, Washington, pp388–390.
53. Gregory, J W. 1896. *Op cit*; pp325–326.
54. Short, J T. 1880. *The North Americans of Antiquity* (New York), 2nd edn, xviii + 544pp; p499.
55. Short, J T. 1880. *Op cit*; p239.
56. Gomara, F L de. 1553. *Conquista de Mexico* (Madrid), 2 vols; vol II, p261.
    Humboldt, A von. 1814. *Researches* (London), 2 vols; vol ii, p16.
57. Bellamy, H S. 1945. *In the Beginning God* (London), 212pp.
58. Bourbourg, Brasseur de. 1864. *Sources de l'histoire primitive du Mexique* (Paris), 146pp; p47.
59. Aston, W G (transl). 1956. *The Nihongi: Chronicles of Japan from Earliest Times to AD 697* (London), xx + 443pp; pp46, 110.
60. Williamson, R W. 1933. *Religious and Cosmic Beliefs of Central Polynesia*, 2 vols, (Cambridge); vol i: p30.
61. Williamson, R W. 1933. *Op cit*; p37.
62. Gray, L H (ed). 1916. H B Alexander in *The Mythology of All Races*, 13 vols, (Boston); vol iv, p362.
    Williamson, R W. 1933. *Op cit*; p41.
63. *Book of Revelation*. Chapt 16, v20–21.
64. *Book of Job*. Chap 38, v.22–23, 29–30.
65. Crawford, J N (transl). 1888. *Kalevala*, 2 vols, (New York); p xiii.
66. Anderson, R B. 1888. *Norse Mythology* (Chicago), 473pp; see p447.
67. Riem, J. 1925. *Die Sintflut in Sage und Wissenschaft* (Hamburg), 196pp.; see p32, 99.

## B. WRITTEN TRADITIONS BY ANCIENT CIVILIZATIONS

### 1. Conflagration Traditions

(From p. 151, Allan and Delair) The Roman account of Ovid tells how a celestial body called *Phaeton* burns entire nations to ashes. The classical Greek writer, Hesiod, illustrates the effects of a giant conflagration that precedes the Deluge. Hesiod's celestial body is called *Typhon*, the Greek name for Phaeton, which spouted great jets of fire from its mouth. The Typhon legend is linked with an early Egyptian cultural name of *Set* which is another name for the Biblical Satan. The Roman writer, Pliny, described Typhon as a terrible comet seen by the people of Egypt and Ethiopia. The king of the period gave his name to the comet which was described as a ball of fire. Flood traditions in Persia blamed a comet, *Tistrya*, as causing the neighboring seas to boil and create a violent hurricane. Many North American traditions described superheated waters and how people jumped into these waters to avoid a very hot atmosphere and immediately died.

The connection to reality is that a celestial, cometary body had a close encounter with Earth. The high-energy electrical discharge from that body heated many water bodies on Earth with its electrical currents which traveled from northern polar regions toward the equator.

### 2. Flood Traditions

(From p. 152, Allan and Delair) Classical Greek traditions cite three different floods: the Deucalion, the Ogyges and the Dardanus. Historians become confused as to which flood came first and is connected to the Great Deluge. I would let Plato simply settle the matter. Plato in his book of *Laws* (Book III) insists that the Flood of Ogyges occurred ten thousand years before his time. In Plato's *Timaeus* (22) and in *Critias* (111-112), he describes the "great deluge of all" as preceding 9000 years of history before his contemporary, Solon. Plato also states that "many great deluges have taken place during the nine thousand years" since the disappearance of Atlantis. (Wikipedia, Ancient Greek flood myths) The other flood or the Flood of Deucalion is thought to occur in the 5th millennium BC. So why are there other "lesser" floods?

This mystery may be answered in various ways. There is no record in ice cores that indicate flooding due to unusual interglacial ice sheet melting which could raise sea level temporarily between the Great Deluge and now. Perhaps local earthquakes and tsunamis in the Mediterranean region occurred during these times. Also, such calamities could have been caused by the Nemesis star system making another visit to the inner solar system and interacting with Earth. If the Sar cycle of every 3600 hundred years for the return of the Nemesis star can be believed, then local crustal disturbances could be associated with its next visits scheduled for 5900 BC and 2300 BC. Another obvious reason for the confusion of other flooding is that interpreters of classical Greek were influenced by Biblical dating that may have compressed the beginning of times to be only 7000 to 5000 years before present.

Noah's Flood, the best known, is obviously incomplete in lacking all the other accompanying calamities. However, the "Book of Revelation" associates the Great Deluge with Satan as the cause, alluding to a war in heaven in which Satan was cast out onto Earth whereupon a great flood issued from his mouth and drowned the whole world. The Noah account has a shared common origin of the Babylonian epic of Gilgamesh which provides many more details such as hail and whirlwinds. This epic has even an earlier origin coming from the Sumerians, who flourished about 4000 to 5000 BC. And, this same epic was also passed to civilizations more eastward who used the Sanskrit language of Pakistan and India.

The Noah story told in various Biblical versions has an unusual twist. The plurality of "Gods" and "Sons of Gods" is retained in these translations. For some reason, the church that controlled the Biblical publications did not cleanse or change these words, although the Christian church leaders were promoting monotheism and the Holy Trinity of one god and his one son. After reading the complete storyline, readers will get the impression that the "Gods" in control of Noah's region fully predicted the pending world catastrophe, like modern man could very well do today. Noah was told to gather all the important domesticated animals and plants and protect them from the flood waters in an ark or enclosed vessel. Noah was also told that his people were being punished for sinful acts made between the Sons of the Gods and the daughters of Man. This statement has the tone of a strict racial prejudice; a distinct perception is that these Gods and man have similar faults in their personalities. After all calamities ended and flood waters receded, the Gods from above rejoined Noah to celebrate with a feast. I presume the Gods and his Sons were held-up in some kind of orbiting space shuttle because they came down from the sky. I encourage your own investigation and go read the Noah account available in most versions of the modern Bible and arrive at your own interpretation. More importantly, I am suggesting that highly technical civilizations existed before the Flood and were mostly destroyed, including accurate memories of them. The residue of memories about this intelligentsia and their knowledge led man to arise and lead his own civilizations for better or for worse.

## 3. Celestial-Disorder Traditions

(From p. 153, Allan and Delair) Ovid's account of this catastrophe has the god Phaeton (the dark planet) riding the Chariot of the Sun. The story includes "loose from its course", "rushed aimlessly" and "snatching the chariot through uncharted ways" that caused the "Cold Bears", the constellations of Ursa Major and Ursa Minor, to plunge into the ocean. This description obviously tells that Earth's axis or its mantle had changed.

Texts by the Chinese stated that "the pillars supporting the sky crumbled and the chains from which the earth was suspended shivered to pieces. Sun, moon, and stars poured down into the northwest, where the sky became low; river, seas and oceans rushed down to the southeast, where the earth sank. A great conflagration burst out. Flood raged." This account is consistent with this paper's hypothesis with the conflagration and crustal disturbances coming before the flood. However, if taken literally, the solar system bodies should have "poured" upward instead of "downward" as is expected by this paper's hypothesis. The waters rushing and earth sinking toward the southeast is a predicted event. Again, the anomalous condition may be a translation or transfer error.

The sagas of the Pawnee Indians of America preserve the notion of important "alpha" stars of constellations changing places, and sagas of the Greenland Eskimos stated that the Earth "rolled over". These verbal transmissions are not precise, but confirm changes in the celestial sky attributed to axial or mantle shifts. Ancient Norse texts, the "Elder Edda" and the "Prose Edda", tell about the saga known as "Ragnarok". The saga explains how two celestial bodies devoured the Sun and Moon in a "rain of dust". This fall of dust, ashes, sand and stones is mentioned in other Scandinavian traditions. The two objects in the sky were possibly the "dark planet" exchanging lightning bolts with Earth and the brown dwarf star hanging in the background.

The Ute Indians of California tell about a conflict of two celestial bodies called Ta-wats and Ta-vi. They fought battles with each other and, then Ta-wats came too close to Earth. A very interesting quotation of metaphors from this saga reveals the "mountain" of arcing plasma discharges released on Earth followed by conflagration and then by flooding. " ... *the sun was shivered into a thousand fragments, which fell to earth causing a general conflagration. Then Ta-wats fled before the burning earth that consumed his feet, consumed his legs, consumed his body, consumed his hands and arms — all were consumed but the head alone, which bowled across the valleys and over mountains, fleeing destruction from the burning earth, until at last, swollen with fear, the eyes of the god burst and the tears gushed over the earth and extinguished the fire."* The symbolism of the consumed body is the initial plasma exchange between Ta-wat and Earth that appeared as one of David Talbott's archetypes called the "stickmen" or "squatter man." The squatter man archetype then converted to either the archetype of either the "mighty mountain" or the "celestial wheel with tongue reaching to Earth". This plasma event is obviously the high-energy arc discharges that electrified the Earth's north polar region and sputtered crustal materials high into the atmosphere.

Allan and Delair also include writings of celestial disturbances by the Greek, Herodotus, who tells how Zeus battles with Typhon and Typhon was struck with bolts of lightning; an Arabian tradition mentions the "Irem of the Columns" destroyed by a thunderous noise and fiery blast from heaven; and Hindu texts refer to aerial explosions.

## 4. Crustal Chaos Traditions

(From p. 155, Allan and Delair) Changes to the Earth's topography are mentioned in many legends. When Earth's crust and mantle are moved as one unit latitudinally by the forces of magnetism, the geoid requires adjustments that not only cause earthquakes and volcanism, but create both uplifting and sinking of tectonic plates on a global scale. This amazing concept that Earth's geoid really did change quickly and dramatically challenges current scientific paradigms and dogma. The following consistent storylines of uplifting and sinking lands throughout separated and supposedly unconnected worldwide cultures provide the undeniable proof to overturn these cherished beliefs of the extremely slow movement of tectonic plates and uplifting of mountain ranges.

Samoan island traditions remember the land sinking into the sea, which overrides that the sea rose above the lands. Tahitian tradition explains how their principal god, Taaroa, became angry with their disobedience to his will and overturned the land into the sea. A few "aurus", projecting points, remained above the sea's surface, to constitute a cluster of currently existing island chains. This type of tradition excludes the Flood concept since their lands never were drained afterward as would happen in a temporary flood. When this author visited the Tahitian Islands, the current island's natural historians explained how their island chain progressed from the oldest to the newest island. The newest island had the largest volcanoes and the oldest had sunk under the sea. Their claim is that volcanoes caused the islands, but the first volcanoes created large enough weight for long enough time that they eventually pushed down the oceanic crust, leaving behind either smaller islands with lower elevations or circular atolls (coral reefs). Coral reefs can only grow in shallow seas that surrounded these sunken islands and still survive today. These natural historians never explained what their traditions stated. These historians were taught by the modern educational system to suspect traditions as being metaphoric instead of being real accounts. I personally believe both of these processes occurred and the initial volcanoes were started by the sinking of shallow lands during the Great Deluge event.

More traditions or myths support this idea of sinking lands in the Pacific Ocean. A pre-Columbian Maya manuscript, the "Troana Codex", describes the land of "Mu" as being a vanished continent residing westward that received numerous convulsive forces that twice upheaved and then suddenly sank forever, killing millions of inhabitants, dating back to 8060 BC before the writing of that manuscript. Hawaiian ancient traditions also account for a continent that stretched from Hawaii to Samoa to Fiji to New Zealand. These lowlands were either called "Ka-houpo-o-Kane" or "Moana-nui-kai-oo", the Great Engulfing Ocean.

The Mixtecs of Mexico also had a similar myth of vanished lands east of their coast in the Caribbean Sea. A sunken civilization close to Cuba was mentioned in a previous chapter about submerged cities, which may be related to the Mixtecs' myth. Interestingly, this myth has the same "twist" as the Noah story. "A great deluge caused the sons and daughters of the gods to perish." This context of the gods and their children living among the other "lesser" inhabitants arises often in so-called myths. Many times, an accompanying idea occurs where the "lesser" peoples are being punished by these calamities for disobeying the gods. These types of memories later become the foundation of religions, emperors, kings and queens for the Great Deluge survivors.

Of course, one cannot forget the most famous sunken ancient land – Atlantis of Plato's "Timaeus" and "Critias". Plato describes this island as being larger than Asia Minor (today's Turkey) and Libya together, sitting in the Atlantic Ocean beyond the Straits of Gibraltar. As outlined, travelers could trek through Atlantis to other islands which were against another large continent. This island of Atlantis had a confederation of great leaders that controlled most of the known lands surrounding the Mediterranean Sea. The story goes on to discuss the flooding, sinking and total destruction of Atlantis, creating an "impassable and unsearchable spot in the ocean blocked by a shoal of mud which the island of Atlantis created as it settled down."

Figure 31. Present Ocean Floor Map Indicates Possibilities for Sunken
Landmasses on Ocean Ridges and in the Western Pacific
Where Only Small Island Chains Now Exist

Much speculation revolves around this story which, knowing more about the technical aspects of the Great Deluge and subsequent geoid adjustments, can hopefully be reduced to a few credible ideas. The first question that arises is why the rulers of the world at that time chose to reside in the middle of the Atlantic Ocean? When one looks at a world map plotting earthquake and active volcano frequency, the Mediterranean basin has more tectonic activity than the middle of the Atlantic Ocean except for the oceanic ridge. Perhaps the most intelligent people of that time thought it was safer to live where they did, thereby isolating themselves not only from terrestrial chaos but also from marauders of the Asian and African continents. Exactly where was Atlantis and what happen to it? It is possible that a shallow land mass connected the Atlantic islands of the Azores, Madieras and Canary Islands. Another possibility that I favor is that a larger landmass straddled the uplifted Atlantic Oceanic Ridge, just as Iceland does today. During the Deluge event, as postulated by Walt Brown in his book, *The Beginning*, the rift pulled apart, releasing hot, pressurized water stored under hydroplates. The ridges then partially sank leaving behind muddy shoals as Plato described. These ridges eventually sank to the ocean bottom after the weight of the higher ocean level finally pushed downward and collapsed the roof of the hydroplates' evacuated reservoirs. Much of the lower-velocity jettisoned muck fell back on the Atlantis' cities and covered them in deep sediments. Only a modern deep ocean search will be able to confirm Plato's writings. Plato's myth now enters the realm of credibility; the search for Atlantis should be even more important than looking for life on other planets.

Besides tectonic plates changing elevation, during antediluvian times, sea level also changed as postulated from (-120) feet from its current average. Hence, the port cities of numerous developed cultures could easily have been built along these old shorelines and been inundated with or without tectonic plate elevation changes. This scenario possibly occurred with major settlements surrounding the Indian Ocean. Sri Lanka and India have traditions of submerged lands and cities. The Selungs of the Mergui Archipelago off southern Burma have legends that waters rose and submerged numerous cities and all their inhabitants. In the case of these unique legends, the lands did not sink; instead, the waters rose.

The indigenous peoples of the Americas tell their traditions as if told by eye-witnesses. The Kato Indians of California describe in recorded words, their Deluge tradition:

*"Every day it rained, every night it rained. All the people slept. The sky fell. The land was not. For a very great distance there was no land. The water of the oceans came together. Animals of all kinds drowned. Where the water went there were no trees … Human beings and animals alike had been washed away… It was very dark."*

The Hopi Indians of the American southwest have an interesting account of the "water serpent deity" who became angry. Their legend is recorded, " … *water spouted up through the 'kivas' [sunken sacred dwellings] and through fireplaces of houses. The earth was rent in great chasms, and water covered everything except one narrow ridge of mud; and across this the serpent deity told all the people to travel."* My personal interpretation is that reptiles, especially snakes, left their flooded dens and swam to what dry land was left and sensed where to go to seek dryer land. The Hopi, being very close to the land and its animals, sensed the snakes knew better where to seek refuge and followed them. The snakes came from deep in the ground where the waters also came due to the rising water table. Hence, the snakes or "serpent deity" was blamed for the tragedy. This legend is a perfect example of how a storyteller of ancient traditions is only passing on the pure imaginations and embellishments of actual events witnessed by past ancestors.

In South America, close to the Andes Mountains, legends arise from tremendous seismic activity – indeed, the uplifting and folding and cross-thrusting of these actual mountains is fully expected by the Deluge hypothesis. The "ring of fire" and its mountain ranges surrounding the Pacific Ocean Basin were caused by the dynamic forces sliding the crust above the Moho layer when the crustal/mantle unit was yanked latitudinally for a brief interval of time. A major uplift of the Andes Mountains ensued as the continental plate rode over top the westerly movement of the oceanic plate. Some witnesses survived. A Peruvian tradition claims the Andes were split apart and deep valleys or "callejons" were formed. A seaport city was risen to the top of the Andes to become the ancient ruins of Tiwanaku near Lake Titicaca in western Bolivia. It is believed that the area was close to sea level because saltwater mineral deposits and shells and fossilized sea animals were found on the Bolivian plateau around the large temple complex of Puma Punku. In fact, a ring of ocean salt deposits, not parallel to its shoreline, surrounds Lake Titicaca. Only a tremendous uplifting could have raised the lake unevenly from its original location near sea level.

The dating of the monument-group of "Puma Punku" is determined to be 500 to 600 A.D. The radiocarbon dating of organic materials in the lowest trenches around these monuments is considered to be the dates of the earliest construction. In addition, it was mentioned that the fill materials in these trenches sat directly on rock and organic materials that were Pleistocene layers. Possibly, the survivors of the Flood who became the Inca culture eventually found and became interested in these ruins around 500 to 600 A.D. and started digging to find buried entrances and treasures. The organic materials left from these early diggings by the Incas were mistakenly labeled as some of the oldest debris of this monument building project when in reality their dates could easily go beyond the Holocene Period and antediluvian times. Archaeologists continually argue about the true dating of these ruins and whether the Inca culture had the skills and tools to build such unbelievable megalith structures. The precision of formed geometric cavities and holes and the finish and levelness of stone surfaces appear to have been machined. My personal up-close inspection of Inca architecture when I visited Ecuador leads me to believe that very advanced or supernatural skills were required to make stones fit together with curved surfaces so closely that not even a piece of paper could fit between. For more information about this topic see *Ancient Technology in Peru and Bolivia* by David Hatcher Childress.[60]

The Andes are very young mountains. Their geology goes back to Pleistocene times with mountain passes lying 4000 meters above sea level and volcanoes attaining great heights.

Everywhere the rugged and jagged peaks remind one of formations created by violent and swift catastrophe. Dr. Walter Bucher of Columbia University is quoted: *"Taken in their entirety, the orogenic belts are the result of worldwide stresses that have acted on the crust as a whole. Certainly, the pattern of these belts is not what one would expect from wholly independent, purely local changes in the crust."* The ruins in Bolivia and on the Nazca Plateau of Peru recount cultural experiences with animals of the sea when indeed the lands are higher than 13,000 feet above sea level and inland. No culture living at such high altitudes with no visible roads of transport should ever have commemorated such deities that are metaphors of the sea unless their lands once upon a time resided very close to the ocean. Perhaps tectonic plate stresses and uplifting were humongous in these regions, leaving behind high on the lifted mountain plateaus a destroyed civilization with their disarray of collapsed megaliths.

## 5. Traditions of Prolonged Darkness

(From p.159, Allan and Delair) The Aztecs of Central America had traditions that a fourth sun was destroyed and the world was plunged into a dark period of twenty-five years. The Akawais of British Columbia speak of a prolonged darkness and intense cold in the world that was illuminated at various intervals by terrifying conflagrations. Similarly, the Japanese and Hawaiians talk about times of continuous darkness. *"...The earth is dancing... Let darkness cease..."* Samoans tell how the "heavens fell down" which is told in the same way by the Dusan tribe of Borneo.

## 6. Hail and Fire Legends are Joined by the Bible and Norse Peoples

(From p. 160, Allan and Delair) The "Book of Joshua" in the Old Testament is quoted: *"From whose womb did the ice come forth, And who has given birth to the hoarfrost of heaven?"* The epic "Kalevala" of Finland describes falls of "hailstones of iron," "red milk" and "blood." The destruction of man came from heaven in the form of fire, stones and ice. Norse sagas following the departure or demise of the "Fenris Wolf" and "Midgard Serpent" detail three winters in succession with no intervening summer. "Ginungagap", a Norse legendary region west and north of Norway became filled with thick and heavy ice and rime with drizzling rain and wind gusts. There was no joy in the Sun.

## C. EVALUATING TRADITIONS

All the aforementioned traditions truly attest to eyewitness accounts of events for all the calamities that occurred or are predicted to have happened prior to, during and after The Great Deluge Event. The stories can no longer be demoted to a series of metaphors, myths, sagas or legends. It must be perfectly understood that these stories are real. These distinctive cultural embellishments can easily be deciphered when the baseline of all these stories are specific calamities that occurred globally. These calamities are borne by natural causes and not by the "Gods" unless the reader wishes, as many ancient writers did, to identify certain celestial bodies, strangers to their skies, as Gods.

These calamities, as witnessed in all these traditions, clearly come from the cometary-like bodies from the sky; the electrification of the crust; high-energy arc discharges, firestorms, bombardment of sand, gravel and stone; grand uplift or sinking of mountains and sea-beds, earthquakes, volcanism, collapsed skies, hurricanes, hailstones, refrigeration and the final act of torrential rains and the deluge.

Peoples' memories, even over thousands of years, are truly impressive and shown to be globally independent recollections. They are sometimes contradictory, yet geographically correct. This paper explains why different types of calamities occur in different regions of Earth. These explanations are not only scientific, but also verified by witness accounts.

## D. FINAL AUTHENTICATION

Authentication for this Great Deluge event for me is the translation of the "Epic Tale of Creation by the Sumerians" by Zecharia Sitchin in his book, *The Twelfth Planet.*[61] Not only does his translation include the flood story, easily recognized as the Biblical Noah story (handed down from high-tech beings to the Sumerians to the Babylonians to the Hebrews), but actually provides the technical reason for its occurrence. God does not directly cause the flood; fate or natural causes are the reason. As you learned, the main reasons are a celestial disturbance of a close encounter and the subsequent sliding of Antarctica's ice sheet into the ocean, as are described in Sitchin's translation. My research ever since the 1980s has led me step-by-step to corroborate this amazing story by gathering more technical reasons and proof. At first, I did not believe Sitchin's assertion that aliens from another planet created our original civilization and us. I originally thought that mankind developed his own civilizations, only to be destroyed one or more times by celestial (asteroids or comets) intruders. After I discovered the Electric Universe group, there are now available technical reasons for alien beings coming from another planet and establishing settlements here on Earth. A brown dwarf star could be a plausible home for such beings if their planet orbited inside a protective glowing sheath of plasma that offered light, heat, and water. Of course, interplanetary travel (interstellar is almost totally impossible) would also be possible, since these beings always traveled with and orbited the Sun. I do not ask you to judge whether our origins came from only our own evolution on this planet or from aliens evolving on another nearby planet orbiting a brown dwarf star that in turn orbited our Sun. Stay open to all ideas – but, of course, favoring you own cherished version. The "mystery dominos" of our genesis will eventually fall into place unless we are too frightened to look further. However, take one small step and ask yourself to judge now whether The Great Deluge is fact or fiction.

# XV.
# ENDNOTES

[1]     "Quick Facts on Ice Sheets"; https://nsidc.org/cryosphere/quickfacts/icesheets.html

[2]     Past sea level – Wikipedia; https://en.wikipedia.org/wiki/Past_sea_level

[3]     Gulf of Cambay – Submerged man-made structures 9,500 years old – Near Dwaraka, Posted on August 14, 2015;
http://ancientexplorers.com/tag/gulf-of-cambay/
"Drowned Indian City could be world's oldest" by Emma Young; *Daily News*, Jan 18, 2002; newscientist.com/article/dn1808-drowned-indian-city-could-be-worlds-oldest/
Gulf of Cambay: Cradle of Ancient Civilization By Badrinaryan; http://archaeologyonline.net/artifacts/cambay

[4]     New Underwater Finds Raise Questions About Flood Myths; Brian Handwerk; for *National Geographic News*, May 28, 2002;
http://news.nationalgeographic.com/news/2002/05/0528_020528_sunkencities.html
"The Quest for the Mythical Submerged Temples of Mahabalipuram" ancient-origins.net/ancient-places-asia/quest-mythical-submerged-temples-mahabalipuram-004504.

[5]     *Sunken Realms: A Complete Catalog of Underwater Ruins* by Karen Mutton; SCB Distributors, 2009

[6]     *British Museum: Secret Treasures of Ancient Egypt: Discover the Sunken Cities* by Kate Sparrow; Nosy Crow Limited, 2016; ISBN 0857637576, 9780857637574

[7]     Dardenelles – Wikipedia; https://en.wikipedia.org/wiki/Dardanelles
Bosphorus – Wikipedia; https://en.wikipedia.org/wiki/Bosphorus

[8]     Bab-el-Mandeb – Wikipedia; https://en.wikipedia.org/wiki/Bab-el-Mandeb

[9]     Map of Strait of Hormuz with maritime political boundaries (2004);
https://en.wikipedia.org/wiki/Strait_of_Hormuz#/media/File:Strait_of_hormuz_full.jpg

[10]    Past sea level – Wikipedia; https://en.wikipedia.org/wiki/Past_sea_level

[11]    Climate: Long range Investigation, Mapping, and Prediction (Climap Project by NOAA paleo collection.
A map of vegetation patterns during the last glacial maximum; Original source has moved. Image seems to be from data used for: Ray, N. and J. M. Adams. 2001. A GIS-based Vegetation Map of the World at the Last Glacial Maximum (25,000-15,000 BP)-(23rd millennium to 13th millennium BC). Internet Archaeology 11.
Below is xfer upload using w:Image:Last glacial vegetation map.png as source. Original uploader information 02:52, 5 May 2005. User:SEWilco (Talk I contribs) ... 782×549 (133,566 bytes) (Last Glacial Maximum Vegetation Reconstructed vegetation cover at the Last Glacial Maximum period ~18,000 years ago-( ~16th millennium BC), describing the type of vegetation cover present, based on fossil pollen samples recovered from lake and bog sediments. Derived from reconstructions by Jonathan Adams in the QEN Atlas, and Ray and Adams (2001). Last Glacial Maximum Vegetation Reconstructed vegetation cover at the Last Glacial Maximum period ~18,000 years ago, describing the type of vegetation cover present, based on fossil pollen samples recovered from lake and bog sediments.

[12]    Chen, J. L.; Wilson, C. R.; Blankenship, D.; Tapley, B. D. (2009). "Accelerated Antarctic ice loss from satellite gravity measurements". *Nature Geoscience*. 2 (12): 859. Bibcode:2009NatGe...2..859C. doi:10.1038/ngeo694

[13]     Younger Dryas – NOAA; ncdc.noaa.gov/abrupt-climate-change/The%20Younger%20Dryas

[14]     "The retreat chronology of the Laurentide Ice Sheet during the last 10,000 years and implications for deglacial sea-level rise" by David Ullman; University of Wisconsin-Madison, Department of Geoscience; http://serc.carleton.edu/vignettes/collection/58451.html
"Paleoclimate over the Laurentide Ice Sheet at the Last Glacial Maximum"; A collaborative research effort by the Byrd Polar Research Center Polar Meteorology Group (PMG) at http://polarmet.osu.edu/ and the University of Maine Institute for Quaternary and Climate Studies at https://sites.umaine.edu/iceage. Supported by NSF OPP-9905381 and NSF OPP-9900477.
University Corporation for Atmospheric Research; http://www.cgd.ucar.edu/ccr/TraCE/images/ice5G-feng-thesis.png or google "Images for ice sheets paleogeography".

[15]     Laurentide Ice Sheet Deglaciation Maps; https://lessthan3ley.files.wordpress.com/2014/06/laurnetide-ice-sheet-deglaciation.jpg

[16]     NOAA (National Climatic Data Center) Paleoclimatology; "A Paleo Perspective on Abrupt Climate Change; ncdc.noaa.gov/abrupt-climate-change/The%20Younger%20Dryas

[17]     Figure of the Earth - Wikipedia; https://en.wikipedia.org/wiki/Figure_of_the_Earth

[18]     "Ice Sheets in Antarctica" by the British Antarctica Survey (BAS); bas.ac.uk/about/antarctica/geography/ice/sheets.php

[19]     Siegert, M.J. Antarctic subglacial topography and ice-sheet evolution. Earth Surface Processes and Landforms 33, 646-660 (2008).
Siegert, M.J., Carter, S., Tabacco, I., Popov, S. & Blankenship, D.D. A revised inventory of Antarctic subglacial lakes. Antarctic Science 17, 453-460 (2005).
http://www.antarcticglaciers.org/modern-glaciers/subglacial-lakes/ Although much of the East Antarctic Ice Sheet is very cold and above pressure melting point, in some places, the ice is so thick that it does reach this magic temperature. In some of the deep troughs, where ice is over 3.5 km (10,500 ft.) thick, pressure melting point is reached. This means that there is water underneath the ice sheet. The East Antarctic Ice Sheet therefore hides a huge number of subglacial lakes, the largest being Subglacial Lake Vostok.

[20]     http://www.antarcticglaciers.org/
Lythe, M.B., Vaughan, D.G., and the BEDMAP Consortium. 2001. BEDMAP: a new ice thickness and subglacial topographical model of Antarctica. Journal of Geophysical Research, 2001. 106(B6): p. 11335-11351.

[21]     Prouty, W. F., 1952, Carolina Bays and their Origin. Geological Society of America Bulletin vol. 63, no. 2, pp. 167–224.
Kaczorowski, R. T., 1977, The Carolina Bays: A Comparison with Modern Oriented Lakes Technical Report no. 13-CRD, Coastal research Division, Department of Geology, University of South Carolina, Columbia, South Carolina. 124 pp.
Coleman, D. (2001) Delmarva Bays: Natural Enigmas. Maryland Department of Natural Resources Archived September 3, 2013, at the Wayback Machine., Annapolis. Maryland.

[22]     *The Electric Universe* by Wallace Thornhill and David Talbott; amazon.com/Electric-Universe-Wallace-Thornhill-Talbott/dp/0977285138

[23]     *Cataclysm! Compelling Evidence of a Cosmic Catastrophe in 9500 B.C.*; By D. S. Allan and J. B. Delair;
http://www.simonandschuster.com/books/Cataclysm!/D-S-Allan/9781879181427

[24]     Giant-impact Hypothesis – Wikipedia: https://en.wikipedia.org/wiki/Giant-impact_hypothesis

[25]     NOAA National Geophysical Data Center. "Wandering of the Geomagnetic Poles". Retrieved October 10, 2011; "Geomagnetism Frequently Asked Questions". NGDC. Retrieved 11 January 2009; British Geological Survey - Magnetic Poles
NOAA National Geophysical Data Center - http://www.ngdc.noaa.gov/geomag/image/south_dip_poles.png
https://en.wikipedia.org/wiki/Geomagnetic_pole

[26]     "Identification of Younger Dryas outburst flood path from Lake Agassiz to the Arctic Ocean"; Julian B. Murton1, Mark D. Bateman2, Scott R. Dallimore3, James T. Teller4 & Zhirong Yang4; Nature 464, 740-743 (1 April 2010) doi:10.1038/nature08954; Received 19 May 2009; Accepted 16 February 2010
[1]Permafrost Laboratory, Department of Geography, University of Sussex, Brighton BN1 9QJ, UK
[2]Sheffield Centre for International Drylands Research, Department of Geography, Winter Street, University of Sheffield, Sheffield S10 2TN, UK

[3]Geological Survey of Canada, 9860 West Saanich Road, Sidney, British Columbia V8L 4B2, Canada

[4]Department of Geological Sciences, University of Manitoba, Winnipeg, Manitoba R3T 2N2, Canada Correspondence to: Julian B. Murton1 Correspondence and requests for materials should be addressed to J.B.M. (Email: j.b.murton@sussex.ac.uk).

"Arctic freshwater forcing of the Younger Dryas cold reversal"; Lev Tarasov and W.R. Peltier; Department of Physics, University of Toronto, Toronto, Ontario, Canada M5S 1A7; Nature 435, 662-665 (2 June 2005) doi:10.1038/nature03617; Received 5 October 2004; Accepted 1 April 2005; Correspondence to: Lev Tarasov1 Correspondence and requests for materials should be addressed to L.T. (Email: lev@atmosp.physics.utoronto.ca).

[27]   Bryan, S.E. (2010). "The largest volcanic eruptions on Earth". *Earth-Science Reviews*. 102 (3-4): 207. Bibcode:2010ESRv..102..207B. doi:10.1016/j.earscirev.2010.07.001.

[28]   http://www.ranker.com/list/the-world_s-6-known-supervolcanoes/analise.dubner

[29]   Steam Explosions, Earthquakes, and Volcanic Eruptions–What's in Yellowstone's Future? - U.S. GEOLOGICAL SURVEY and the NATIONAL PARK SERVICE-OUR VOLCANIC PUBLIC LANDS; U.S. Geological Survey; Fact Sheet 2005-3024; https://pubs.usgs.gov/fs/2005/3024/

[30]   Introduction to hydrothermal (steam) explosions in Yellowstone. Yellowstone National Park. Yellowstone Net. Retrieved December 31, 2008.

[31]   Carlson, A. E. (2013). "The Younger Dryas Climate Event" (PDF). *Encyclopedia of Quaternary Science*. 3. Elsevier. pp. 126–34.

[32]   Aitken, M.J. (1990). *Science-based Dating in Archaeology*. London: Longman. ISBN 0-582-49309-9.
Aitken, Martin J. (2003). "Radiocarbon Dating". In Ellis, Linda. *Archaeological Method and Theory*. New York: Garland Publishing. pp. 505–508.
Libby, W.F. (1946). "Atmospheric helium three and radiocarbon from cosmic radiation". Physical Review. 69 (11–12): 671–672. Bibcode:1946PhRv...69..671L. doi:10.1103/PhysRev.69.671.2.
Anderson, E.C.; Libby, W.F.; Weinhouse, S.; Reid, A.F.; Kirshenbaum, A.D.; Grosse, A.V. (1947). "Radiocarbon from cosmic radiation". Science. 105 (2765): 576–577. Bibcode:1947Sci...105..576A. doi:10.1126/science.105.2735.576. PMID 17746224.

[33]   Bowman, Sheridan (1995) [1990]. *Radiocarbon Dating*. London: British Museum Press. ISBN 0-7141-2047-2

[34]   Bowman, Sheridan (1995) [1990]. *Radiocarbon Dating*. London: British Museum Press. ISBN 0-7141-2047-2; pp. 24–27.
Suess, H.E. (1970). "Bristlecone-pine calibration of the radiocarbon time-scale 5200 B.C. to the present". In Olsson, Ingrid U. *Radiocarbon Variations and Absolute Chronology*. New York: John Wiley & Sons. pp. 303–311

[35]   Aitken (1990), pp. 85–86.

[36]   Aitken (1990), p. 59.
Taylor, R.E.; Bar-Yosef, Ofer (2014). *Radiocarbon Dating* (2nd ed.). Walnut Creek, California: Left Coast Press. ISBN 978-1-59874-590-0.; pp. 74–75.

[37]   Libby, Willard F. (1965) [1952]. *Radiocarbon Dating* (2nd (1955) ed.). Chicago: Phoenix; p. 6.
Bowman (1995), pp. 24–27.
Cronin, Thomas M. (2010). *Paleoclimates: Understanding Climate Change Past and Present*. New York: Columbia University Press. ISBN 978-0-231-14494-0.; p. 35.

[38]   Bowman (1995), pp. 24–27.

[39]   NOAS (National Climatic Data Center) Paleoclimatology; "A Paleo Perspective on Abrupt Climate Change; ncdc.noaa.gov/abrupt-climate-change/The%20Younger%20Dryas
Climate changes associated with the Younger Dryas, highlighted here by the light blue bar, include (from top to bottom): cooling and decreased snow accumulation in Greenland, cooling in the tropical Cariaco Basin, and warming in Antarctica. Also shown is the flux of meltwater from the Laurentide Ice Sheet down the St. Lawrence River. Sources: Alley (2000), Lea et al. (2003), EPICA Community Members (2004), and Licciardi et al. (1999).

[40]     Ice Cores and the Age of the Earth by Larry Vardiman, Ph.D.; http://www.icr.org/article/ice-cores-age-earth/
         Hammer, C.U., H.B. Clausen, W. Dansgaard, N. Gundestrup, S.J. Johnsen, and N. Reeh. 1978. "Dating of Greenland ice cores by flow models,
         isotopes, volcanic debris, and continental dust." *Journal of Glaciology*, 20:3.

[41]     Jouzel, J. and L. Merlivat, 1984. "Deuterium and oxygen 18 in precipitation: modeling of the isotopic effects during snow formation." *Journal of
         Geophysical Research*, 89:11, 749.

[42]     Lorius, C., J. Jouzel, C. Ritz, L. Merlivat, N.I. Barkov, Y.S. Korotkevich, and V.M. Kotlyakov, 1985. "A 160,000-year climatic record from Antarctic
         ice." *Nature*, 316:591.

[43]     Composite data for Dome C, CO2 levels (ppm) going back nearly 800,000 years related to glacier cycles;
         Data from ncdc.noaa.gov: Composite CO2 record (0-800 kyr BP), marked up with 230 ppm transition between glacial and interglacial
         periods; ice core data estimates of atmospheric CO2 over the last 800 millennia.

[44]     East Antarctica Ice Sheet by Bethan Davies (last updated 3/3/2014; http://www.antarcticglaciers.org/antarctica/east-antarctic-ice-sheet/)

[45]     Oard, M.J., 1990. "An Ice Age Caused by the Genesis Flood." ICR Monograph, 243 pp.

[46]     https://en.wikipedia.org/wiki/Subglacial_lake

[47]     Ivins E.R., (2009) Ice sheet stability and sea level, Science, 324, 888-889.
         Lythe, Matthew B.; Vaughan, David G. (June 2001). "BEDMAP: A new ice thickness and subglacial topographic model of Antarctica". Journal
         of Geophysical Research. 106 (B6): 11335–11352. Bibcode:2001JGR...10611335L. doi:10.1029/2000JB900449.

[48]     Glacial Landsystems/James Ross Island by Bethan Davies (et al. 2013); http://www.antarcticglaciers.org/glacial-geology/glacial-
         landforms/glacial-landsystems-on-james-ross-island/
         http://www.ingentaconnect.com/content/igsoc/jog/2012/00000058/00000212/art00013

[49]     Marine Ice Sheet Instability by Bethan Davies (last updated 06/19/2014); AntarcticGlaciers.org; http://www.antarcticglaciers.org/glaciers-
         and-climate/ice-ocean-interactions/marine-ice-sheets/

[50]     Ollier, C.D. "Australian Landforms and their History". National Mapping Fab. Geoscience Australia.
         Burrows, C. J.; Moar, N. T. (1996). "A mid Otira Glaciation palaeosol and flora from the Castle Hill Basin, Canterbury, New Zealand" (PDF 340
         Kb). *New Zealand Journal of Botany*. 34 (4): 539–545. doi:10.1080/0028825X.1996.10410134

[51]     800,000-year Ice-Core Records of Atmospheric Carbon Dioxide (CO2)/Graphics/800,000-year record from Dome C;
         http://cdiac.ornl.gov/trends/co2/ice_core_co2.html

[52]     *In the Beginning: Compelling Evidence for Creation and the Flood*, by Dr. Walt Brown. Copyright © Center for Scientific Creation;
         http://www.creationscience.com/onlinebook/IntheBeginningTOC.html

[53]     "Novosibirsk climate". Worldclimate.com. 4 February 2007. Retrieved 15 May 2010.
         "Omsk climate". Worldclimate.com. 4 February 2007. Retrieved 15 May 2010.
         "Kazachengoye climate". Worldclimate.com. 4 February 2007. Retrieved 15 May 2010

[54]     Lioubimtseva E.U., Gorshkov S.P. & Adams J.M.; A Giant Siberian Lake During the Last Glacial: Evidence and Implications; Oak Ridge
         National Laboratory
         C. Michael Hogan. 2011. Taiga. eds. M.McGinley & C.Cleveland. Encyclopedia of Earth. National Council for Science and the Environment.
         Washington DC.

[55]     Walter KM, Zimov SA, Chanton JP, Verbyla D, Chapin FS (September 2006). "Methane bubbling from Siberian thaw lakes as a positive
         feedback to climate warming". Nature. 443 (7107): 71–5. doi:10.1038/nature05040. PMID 16957728.
         Seth Borenstein (7 September 2006). "Scientists Find New Global Warming 'Time Bomb'". Associated Press.

[56]     *Cataclysm! Compelling Evidence of a Cosmic Catastrophe in 9500 B.C.*; By D. S. Allan and J. B. Delair; 1995

[57] *The Electric Universe*, May 24, 2007; by Wallace Thornhill and David Talbott; amazon.com/Electric-Universe-Wallace-Thornhill-Talbott/dp/0977285138
The Thunderbolts Project ™, thunderbolts.info/wp/resources/

[58] http://www.thunderbolts.info/wp/eu-guides; Episode 3; Symbols of an Alien Sky: The Lightning Scarred Planet, Mars by Thunderbolt Projects.

[59] *The Saturn Myth: A Reinterpretation of Rites and Symbols Illuminating Some of the Dark Corners of Primordial Society* Hardcover – 1980 by David N Talbott.

[60] *Ancient Technology in Peru and Bolivia* Paperback – November 15, 2012 by David Hatcher Childress; amazon.com/Ancient-Technology-Bolivia-Hatcher-Childress/dp/1935487817.

[61] *Twelfth Planet: Book I of the Earth Chronicles* (The Earth Chronicles) by Zecharia Sitchin; amazon.com/Twelfth-Planet-Book-Earth-Chronicles/dp/0061379131

# ABOUT THE AUTHOR

The Moon-Earth enigma has been a lifetime pursuit since the mid-80's for Doug Ettinger, born in 1944 in Pen Argyl, Pennsylvania. Doug graduated from Lehigh University with a B.S. in mechanical engineering and has retired after a 22-year career in nuclear engineering. He has two sons and currently lives in Pittsburgh, Pennsylvania, with his significant other, Rhonda Smith. Some of his main interests and distractions are snow skiing, hiking, kayaking, sailing, bicycling, tennis, ballroom dancing, movies, and chess.

Doug wrote his initial journals about the Moon enigma; NASA is still plagued with how the Moon and Earth became a system. His original writings were divided into three hypotheses: Earth's Metamorphosis (EMM) hypothesis (about Earth's collision with a rogue planet and transferring orbits); Collocation of Stars and Planets (CSP) hypothesis (about how planets seek their orbits and stars find binary companions); and Supernovae Seeding (SNS) hypothesis (about how new stars and planets are birthed through the expulsion of supernova ejecta). His passion and self-training crosses many fields of science including astronomy, astrophysics, planetary science, oceanography, physics, geophysics, and particle physics. Hopefully, his depth of knowledge in this wide spectrum of disciplines is adequate to at least meet the minimum of academic standards.

His initial interest started with reading about solar system formation and all the unexplained anomalies that exist. One of these anomalies, the Moon enigma, caught his attention after reading Isaac Asimov's claim that the Moon is actually a planet. Combining the anomaly of the asteroid belt led Doug to consider the ideas for his Earth's Metamorphosis hypothesis.

Doug helped his one son with his science fair project by providing a primitive computer program that could create your own stellar systems or modify the starting conditions of the solar system and then run the program for a given amount of time to determine the end conditions. His son's project was taken to a higher level of competition at a university. The judge explained that his criteria for collisions were invalid because the two-body problem and calculus can prove otherwise. His son did not know how to defend his position by explaining the limitations of the two-body problem. Several months later a comet broke up and crashed into Jupiter for everybody to see. These unfolding scenarios were the seed that finally launched Doug on his way to resolve the Moon enigma.

Since posting my original journals and some subsequent editions in 2013, many new developments and ideas have occurred. Also, some power point presentations have been included to aid teachers who wish their students to sometimes think outside the present box of paradigms.

Special attention was given to the Sun's sister star, currently named Nemesis, which at the time, was being hunted by space telescopes. I wanted better reasons for mass extinction events. The accepted notion of a very long period star orbiting the Sun and infrequently disturbing an imaginary Oort Cloud of comets was not believable or proven. NASA has recently revised or given-up their model. The disturbances of this star are now considered to be perturbations of the newly discovered Kuiper Belt objects. Doug slowly and cautiously became convinced that a much closer, very dim brown dwarf star orbited the Sun and intersected the orbits of the Sun's planets, causing occasional chaos. The underpinning of this idea originated with Zecharia Sitchin's book, *The Twelfth Planet,* that involved a planet with moons that orbited the Sun every 3600 years.

Doug adapted his idea by making Sitchin's intruding planet become a brown dwarf star with its own set of planets. This idea easily dovetailed into his postulation of "Earth's Metamorphosis" found in his original journal. The Earth's "Great Deluge" is linked with one of Nemesis's crossings of the inner solar system, which is well dated to be 11,500 years BP, at the end of the Younger Dryas geological period. This led to investigating other crossings at approximate intervals of every 3600 years in the journal "A Brief History of Mankind's Chaotic Past".

Subsequently, Doug discovered the ideas formulated by a group of independent scientists called the "Electric Universe". Their concepts unbelievably corroborated his journal by indicating an electrified and magnetic brown dwarf star periodically enters our solar system. This star, and/or its planets, interacts with the Sun's planets, producing scarring and giant pitting through gigantic arc discharges that are readily observable with NASA's space probes and telescopes. The "Electric Universe" also provided a convincing dialogue, via comparative mythology, that humans witnessed and recorded many of these events.

After taking an Alaskan cruise and talking with the indigenous people, called the Tlingit, I learned that their very distinct tribal cedar dug-out canoe docking systems are found not only at sea level, but at locations 200 to 250 feet above the ocean on the mountain side. The Tlingit flood tradition and this recognition triggered my next journal "The Great Deluge:

Fact or Fiction?". Doug combined the ideas of other books written about the Flood, including the exclusion of some of their incongruent arguments. He added the idea that one of Nemesis's planets had a close encounter with Earth that caused many calamities, such as a huge arc discharge that destroyed the Laurentide Ice Sheet and initiated the Noah Flood, which is found in other flood traditions throughout the world.

One of the difficulties for the "Electric Universe" is convincing consensus science that "charge separation" or flow of segregated electrons and electrical current flow through space do exist. This gave me ideas about how these phenomena are possible by establishing the idea of "electron asymmetry" in a journal by the same name. "Electron asymmetry" not only helps to explain "charge separation" and high energy arc discharges between close encounters of celestial bodies, but provides the reason for why gravity exists.

## CONNECT WITH DOUG ETTINGER

Contact me at email: dougettinger@verizon.net
Learn and read other articles: EttingerJournals.com
Friend me at Facebook: https://www.facebook.com/Star-Planetary-Origins

## RELATED ARTICLES BY DOUG ETTINGER

- The Enigma of the Giza Pyramids of Egypt – When and How Were these Megaliths Designed and Built (ettingerjournals.com/dbe_giza.shtml)

- Corroborating Massive Solar Eruption Causing Catastrophism on Earth – Using Robert Johnson's Model for Providing Enough Energy to Cause Tectonic Uplift Processes through Thermal Expansion and Phase Change of Rocks – (ettingerjournals.com/dbe_solar_eruptions.shtml)

- A Brief History of Mankind's Chaotic Past – Post-Paleolithic Times (20,000 Years Ago) to the Present that embraces Nemesis' Influence and Prophecy – (ettingerjournals.com/dbe_mankind.shtml)

- Ancient Sun-God Descriptions Give Proof for an Orbiting Nemesis Star – A Comparative Study of Mesopotamian and Egyptian Sun-God Depictions Referenced in an Ev Cochrane Article (ettingerjournals.com/dbe_sun_gods.shtml)

- Problems with the Saturn Myth's Polar Configuration – Replacing the Proto-Planet Saturn Idea with an Orbiting Brown Dwarf Star (ettingerjournals.com/dbe_saturn_myth.shtml)

- Electron Asymmetry – What is this Asymmetry? How Does It Affect Our Universe? (ettingerjournals.com/dbe_electron_asymmetry.shtml)

- Earth's Metamorphosis (EMM) Hypothesis – The Event and Aftermath of Earth's Collision with a Large Impactor that Changes Its Orbit, Spin Axis, and Surface Features (ettingerjournals.com/dbe_emm.shtml)